Winifred Ellen

Christmas 1916.

from "Bougival".

MADE IN THE TRENCHES

"Well, if you knows of a better 'ole, go to it."

MADE IN THE TRENCHES

COMPOSED ENTIRELY FROM ARTICLES &
SKETCHES CONTRIBUTED BY SOLDIERS

EDITED BY

SIR **FREDERICK TREVES**, BT.

G.C.V.O., C.B., LL.D.

Serjeant Surgeon to His Majesty the King

AND

GEORGE GOODCHILD

ALL PROFITS ACCRUING FROM THE SALE OF
THIS BOOK ARE TO BE DEVOTED TO THE
"STAR AND GARTER" ENDOWMENT FUND IN AID
OF TOTALLY DISABLED SOLDIERS AND SAILORS

LONDON: GEORGE ALLEN & UNWIN LTD.

RUSKIN HOUSE   40 MUSEUM STREET, W.C.

First published in 1916

PREFACE

THE primary object of this book is to assist the funds of the "Star and Garter" Home for totally disabled soldiers and sailors. The present temporary building gives a Home to sixty-five soldiers and sailors, all of whom have been paralysed by being shot through the spine or brain with the exception of two seamen whose backs were broken when their ships were torpedoed. The Home is always full and many are waiting for admission.

In the aftermath of this grievous war there is no more lamentable and pathetic figure than the soldier who, by reason of his wounds, is paralysed and left utterly helpless. One is apt to associate such helplessness with extreme old age or with the final phase of some exhausting illness; but here is a man in the very flower of his youth, bedridden possibly for life, unable to move hand or foot, and dependent, at every moment of the day, upon the ministration of others.

In the paralysis of old age there is usually, coincident with the loss of power, a merciful decay of the brain, a loss of mind that merges into mere apathy and oblivion. In the case of the stricken soldier, however, the mind is as vigorous and as alert as ever; the eagerness and independence of youth are still aglow in the brain; there are still the intense longing to do, the stimulus to venture, the desire to lay hold of the joys of life; while with this mental energy is associated a body that cannot feel, limbs that cannot move, fingers without touch, and hands as listless as the hands of the dead.

In the headlong rush of the bayonet charge there has been a sudden stab of pain, and the man of arms, terrible in his strength, has become in a moment feebler than a child.

Let the people of this country, who are safe and sound, remember that it was in fighting for England that such dire ruin fell upon these men and that it rests with those for whom they fought to afford them whatever comfort it is within the power of man to bestow.

After every form of treatment has been attempted and failed, the soldier who is the subject of severe paralysis is retired from the Army with a small pension. It is generally assumed that he will return to his friends to end his days, and that his pension will defray the cost of his maintenance and care. In the average case this is an impossible position. That he will be treated in his home with affectionate devotion none will doubt, but in cases such as these something more than devotion is needed, if the patient's life is to be prolonged and if he is to be spared from suffering while life lasts.

He will need skilled and indeed special nursing ; he will require a particular type of bed, together with appliances which are not within the reach of the poor and are not capable of being handled by the untrained. The cottage bedroom is often small and cramped, and in every way unsuited for the care of cases of this type. The possibility of taking advantage of any but the simplest measure of treatment is slight, while the prospect of a bed being moved, day by day, into the open air is very remote. When the difficulties and disadvantages are grasped and found insuperable, one knows what happens—the patient is moved to the wards of a workhouse infirmary, and there his career comes to an end with little glory to those who say that the wounded soldier shall lack for nothing,

6

and that England is grateful to all who have fought for her freedom.

By the generosity of the members of the Auctioneers' and Estate Agents' Institute of the United Kingdom, the "Star and Garter" Hotel, on Richmond Hill, was purchased for presentation to H.M. The Queen. The Queen—devoted as Her Majesty is to whatever concerns the sick and wounded—was deeply moved by the knowledge that a large number of our soldiers and sailors were lying in various hospitals paralysed. Her Majesty was graciously pleased to hand over this important building to the British Red Cross Society, and has expressed a wish that, under the control and management of that Society, it should be devoted to the care of such totally disabled men as are retired from the Service.

The building, by the gate of Richmond Park, is at a convenient distance from London, and occupies a site unrivalled from the standpoint of health, while the view from the house and the gardens is famous for its beauty throughout the world.

The patients—sixty-five in number—are at present housed in the spacious annexe of the old Hotel. The most modern medical measures are pursued in order to secure some improvement in their condition, and the staff have had the supreme satisfaction of seeing—within the last six months—no less than five men *walk* out of the "Star and Garter" on their way home.

A new "Star and Garter," on the present site, is in process of erection. It is to be built and equipped entirely by the women of England. The British Women's Hospital Fund has most nobly and generously supplied the whole of the necessary funds. What is now needed is an Endowment Fund to maintain the building for all time. To that Fund the proceeds of this Book will be devoted.

The new building is being designed by Mr. G. Gilbert

Made in the Trenches

Scott, the architect of the Liverpool Cathedral, who is most generously giving his services gratuitously to the British Red Cross Society.

The new building will be a Permanent Memorial of the work of the Red Cross rendered by the generous-hearted people of England to our sick and wounded in the Great War. It will be the Women's Memorial of the Great War. It will be dedicated, for all time, to the disabled, crippled, or helpless soldier or sailor. It will be his home. It will be a refuge for him as well in times of peace as in times of war, and it is Her Majesty's pleasure that it should always retain the name of the "Star and Garter." It will accommodate some 270 men.

When completed the "Star and Garter" will possess a ward for the bedridden, which, when the land is at peace, will be reduced, it is hoped, to comparatively small dimensions. The larger part of the building will be devoted to quarters for men who are no longer able to work or to help themselves, and who, without such a home, would find their way, in many instances, to the workhouse infirmary. Each man will have his own room adequately equipped with all that he will want. There will be central heating and central cooking, a dining room, smoking room, reading room, and recreation room.

The garden will be restored, and not a foot of it will be encroached upon. The helpless man as he lies in bed will be able to look over the Thames Valley and that glorious stretch of wooded country which is bounded only by the Surrey Hills and the Great Park of Windsor.

The "Star and Garter" will, in fact, become the soldier's Hampton Court Palace where, by the generosity of the men and women of the country, he will find peace and comfort for his declining years. It will be his last home. It can be made worthy of him if the people of England will make it worthy of the country he has done his best to serve.

8

Preface

He has fought his fight, he has met his fate ; let him feel that the loving-kindness of the land for which he died is around him when the bugle, from afar off, summons him to " The Last Post."

FREDERICK TREVES.

POSTSCRIPT.—*I wish to make it clear, and for the relief of my conscience to state, that my position of Editor has been purely nominal. The whole of the work of the book—the collecting and selection of materials—has been carried out by Mr. George Goodchild alone, with infinite pains and with a hearty goodwill.*

To him the gallant men in the " Star and Garter " owe a debt of gratitude, and that gratitude is his reward.

EDITORIAL NOTE

I wish to make it clear that my aim throughout has been not so much to make this volume a work of great literary or artistic merit, as to give a really representative idea of the life and thought of the Army as a whole. While a certain proportion of its contents does, I believe, merit praise purely from an artistic point of view, other contributions have been included on the score of their interest alone, and the whole, I hope, goes some way towards fulfilling the object I had in view.

I am much indebted to the editors of *The Gasper*, *The Listening Post*, *The Iodine Chronicle*, *The Searchlight*, *The 3rd London General Hospital Gazette*, *The Sphere*, *The Daily Mail*, *The Evening News*, &c., for their kindness in allowing me to reproduce certain articles and sketches from the pages of their respective journals.

In particular, I am delighted to be able to include the very fine poems of Corporal Streets, for which courtesy I am indebted to Mr. Galloway Kyle, editor of *The Poetry Review*.

The cover design by Bert Thomas is reproduced by kind permission of *The Weekly Despatch* Tobacco Fund.

G. G.

CONTENTS

	PAGE
PREFACE	5
THE BLIGHTY SQUAD	15
AT THE CROSS ROADS	25
THE MAKING OF MICKY McGHEE	31
THE OASIS	39
A LAMENT	45
THE SENSITIVE PLANT	49
THAT BLOKE BATES	61
WITH THE BOMBARDIERS	64
THE NEO-TROGLODYTES	67
IN THE TRENCHES	74
ANZAC SLANG	78
LEAVES FROM A SOLDIER'S DIARY	81
BALM IN GILEAD	94
TOMMY ATKINS, LINGUIST	97
"AT NIGHT-TIDE"	103
LETTER FROM A WOUNDED RUSSIAN SOLDIER TO HIS FAMILY	104
A SHAKESPEARE TERCENTENARY IN THE TRENCHES	106
HUMOROUS SIDES OF THE WAR: "WHO ARE THE PRISONERS TO-DAY?"	112
"SECTION FIVE"	114
ACTIVE SERVICE	116
HOW ISCHAN PACHA WAS CAPTURED BY—THE DEVIL!	117
"'COUNTED FOR"	120
SAINT PATRICK'S DAY IN THE MORNIN'	124
HALF AN HOUR ON THE PARADE GROUND	129
OFF TO BLIGHTY!	132

Contents

	PAGE
THROUGH A SENTRY'S EYES	133
THE "WORKING PARTY"	138
TOLD IN A DUG-OUT	141
THE BARRICADE	144
"A LONELY SOLDIER"	147
THE CONVOY	150
POEMS OF LIFE AND DEATH	154
LIFE ON AN ARMOURED TRAIN	163
THE GARDEN OF SLEEP	167
WORDY ECONOMY	171
TUBBY	178
THE "SURE-TO-BE-HIT" FEELING	180
MAKING IT CLEAR	185
HINTS FOR WAR BRIDES	189
THE SPECTRE	192
TOLD IN A DUG-OUT	196
THE MOANER	198
THE PADRE	200
SOLILOQUY OF PRIVATE SELKIRK	205
THE WINGED HUN	207
TOLD IN A DUG-OUT	211
"THE BULL RING"	213
A SERGEANT'S VOICE	217
WHAT WE FIND IN THE GERMAN TRENCHES	218
HOW A GERMAN BATTALION PERISHED	221
6-IN. Q.F.	225
OUT WITH A NIGHT PATROL	230
SUZETTE DISCUSSES THE SAPPERS	232
A GLIMPSE OF WAR	236

ILLUSTRATIONS

"WELL, IF YOU KNOWS A BETTER 'OLE, GO TO IT" . . *Frontispiece*

PAGE

MEN'S WEAR 21

THOSE WHO *SHOULD* WRITE ABOUT IT! 22

THOSE WHO *DO* WRITE ABOUT IT! 23

"SHUN" 24

"VE'RE DUN," 1916 29

THE CLUTCHING HAND 30

MICKY McGHEE 33

"—AND THEN THEY CHARGED US!" 37

FORGETTING THEIR PAINS 44

"CAME UPON A GREAT TOAD WITH MAGNIFICENT JEWEL-LIKE EYES" . 53

ADVICE TO YOUNG "SUBS" 62

A MISINTERPRETATION 63

"SQUADDIES" 71

"WITH THE ARMY." (I) TEACHING RECRUITS TO "CARRY THE LEFT FOOT
    12 INCHES TO THE LEFT" 73

C'EST MAGNIFIQUE!—MAIS CE N'EST PAS LA GUERRE . . . 75

BLIMY! 77

AN ANZAC CONVALESCENT 78

GALLIPOLI 79

IN HOSPITAL 80

THE MISSING BANANA SKIN 92, 93

Illustrations

PAGE

"AND THE WOODBINE SPICES ARE WAFTED ABROAD" . *facing page* 97

"ON THE RIGHT FORM—SQUAD!" 99

YEOMEN'S LIFE IN EGYPT . . . . . 100—2

CHANGES IN WHITEHALL 110

"WITH THE ARMY." (2) TELLING OFF A PLATOON . . 111

"WITH THE ARMY." (3) DERBY RECRUIT BEING MEASURED FOR THE UNIFORM 119

"LIGHT DUTY" 121

MEMORIES OF GALLIPOLI 122, 123

SKETCHES FROM FLANDERS 127

A HINT TO SPECULATORS 128

"WE CAN ALWAYS HAVE A GOOD WASH IN THE TRENCHES" . 140

"HI! JOCK—THEY'RE STEALING YOUR CAKE!" . . . 146

AN AWKWARD MOMENT 149

THINGS WE MAY HOPE TO SEE 152, 153

AN AMBULANCE CONVOY 179

THE "BLUES" 210

HOOCH! 216

SEEN IN THE SOMME REGION 224

Ornamental headings, tail-
pieces, &c., by Vernon Lorimer,
Lt. A. D'Egville, Denis Cowles, &c.

MADE IN THE TRENCHES

THE BLIGHTY SQUAD BY BOYD CABLE

THERE were about a dozen men collected in the deep dug-out under what before the advance that morning had been the German front line trench. They were all casualties, men of various regiments and one German prisoner wounded in the head and arm. To those of the others who were not too severely wounded to be concerned in their surroundings, the German was an object of intense interest—an interest that quite overshadowed their wounds, their probable movements, or even the progress of the battle which still rumbled and roared within half a mile of their shelter. It was a huge disappointment to all that the German could speak no English, and some of them were inclined to feel a good deal aggrieved by that fact.

"Disgustin', I call it," said Little Peter. "Ever since I was a kid at school I've 'ad it crammed into me 'ow clever the Germans was, and 'ow keen they was to eddicate themselves. And 'ere the first time I meets one I finds 'e don't know a blessed word of English, even."

"P'raps," said a Cockney rifleman, "'e knows a bit o' French. Now then the French scholards—forward, please. Can't somebody try a bit of French on 'im?"

"I'll have a try if you shove him this way," put in a

1 "Blighty" (The Hindustani *Belati*) = Home, England.

15

Highlander, who was seated in a corner with a bootless and bandaged foot stuck out in front of him.

The German was invited by pantomime to move over to the corner. He went reluctantly, and in some evident doubts as to what was to happen to him.

" Now, Fritz," said Little Peter, " you squat 'ere. Squattey-vous ! No, that's French, an' we dunno yet if 'e savvies French. 'Ere !"—and he pointed and signed until the German understood and sat.

" What'll I ask him ? " said the Scot.

" Ask wot's 'is name first," said the Cockney, and after careful thinking the Scot said slowly and distinctly, " Quel—ay—votrey—nom, moor—see ? "

The German looked at him blankly, and on the question being repeated in louder and more determined tones, shook his head.

The Scot had an inspiration. " Parlez-vous Français ? " he demanded briskly and confidently. The German shook his head in evident non-comprehension again, and at that the Cockney burst out indignantly—

" Fair disgustin', that's wot it is. Why, I know the meanin' of ' Parley-voo Frongsay' myself, and 'ere this bloomin' Germ' 'asn't an idea of it. Eddication ! G'lord, wait till I 'ears any one talk about German eddication again ! Lot o' blanky ignoramuses I call 'em."

A series of muffled crashes outside interrupted the discussion, and immediately after a couple of R.A.M.C. orderlies descended the dug-out steps hastily.

" They've started bumping 'em down again back 'ere," explained one. " So we'd better wait a bit before moving."

" Just as you says," remarked the rifleman indifferently. " I will say these Boshies know 'ow to make a good safe dug-out, an' I'd as soon be 'ere as out amongst the ' crumps.' I've got my Blighty one all right, an' I don't want to cop another packet now that might put me out for the full count."

That undoubtedly expressed the sentiment of all the others —that having been wounded and being therefore due for a trip home, it would be particularly hard luck to be hit again and perhaps killed. So they waited quite contentedly until it was considered reasonably safe to move.

" How long do you reckon it'll be before we're back in Blighty, chum ? " asked one man, and all, even the most severely wounded, awaited the answer of the R.A.M.C. orderly with evident interest.

" It's about an hour's walk back, or a little more, p'raps, to where the ambulance'll pick you up," said the orderly. " Then say two or three hours on the motor to the Field 'Ospital. You might stay there the night or they might rush you straight through to the Red Cross train, and you should be in London within twenty hours o' that."

" So we might be there by to-morrow night ? "

" Easy," said the orderly. " Seein' there's a tidy-sized scrap goin' on they're sure to be evacuatin' the casualties as fast as they can run 'em through."

" To-morrow night," said the Cockney rapturously. " Lumme, just think of it ! We might be seein' the old 'buses runnin' down the Strand an' the lights shinin' on the wet pavement o' Piccadilly Circus to-morrow night. . . ."

" Roll on with it," said a weak voice from the back of the dug-out. " I've 'ad enough o' this."

" How's that bandage ? " asked the orderly. " Feel any-ways easy ? "

" Might be worse," said the man. He lay full length on a stretcher with glimpses of blood-stained bandages showing under the remains of shirt and tunic that had been cut off him and re-wrapped about him after his wounds were dressed. " But I fancies it ain't the bandage as much as the 'ole behind it. But I can stick it easy enough."

There was a moment's lull in the talk, and through it the angry clamour of battle throbbed and beat down to them in their underground refuge. For some minutes past there had been none of those muffled crashes and quivering earth tremors that told of high-explosive shells bursting near, and the orderlies crawled up the steep entrance stairs again to reconnoitre and to estimate the wisdom of making a start.

B

"It's rainin' like billy-oh," they reported on their return, "an' the trenches is gettin' mucky as a mud-pie. It'll be slow goin', especially wi' the stretcher cases—slow an' a bit jolty, I dessay."

"We can stick that," said a young smooth-faced lad with a shell-smashed shoulder. "An' I 'opes we get on with it. I've a urgent appointment in Lunnon, an' if we waits 'ere much longer I might miss the connection."

"P'raps it won't be a London 'ospital you'll go to," said another man ; but at that suggestion the boy scoffed. "I knows just where I'm goin' to," he said. "Might a'most say I've got me bed picked. I was three months there last time I was casualtied, an' I fixed it all up wi' the Sisters to come back to 'em next time."

"An' in the Army they allus allows a man to do just wot 'e 'as fixed up, of course," said the other sarcastically.

"But this ain't Army business, y'see," said the boy triumphantly. "It's Red Cross, an' they runs things mighty different from Army fashion, thank 'Eaven."

"How did you like being in hospital ? " he was asked. "Bit dull, ain't it ? "

"Like it ? Dull ? " exclaimed the boy, and launched out on a pæan of thanksgiving and praise to the hospitals, the doctors, the Sisters, the hospital train, the ship, to all that ran or moved or stood still under the sign of the Red Cross.

"I never want to go to 'eaven if I can stop on in a 'ospital," he said finally. "But if ever I do go I'll 'ave plenty o' good company—an' that's every Sister I ever knowed an' thousands I 'aven't knowed."

There was a lull in the talk when he finished. Every man there was suffering from the pain of wounds, from bodily fatigue, from the cold clammy chill of wet mud-caked clothing, the oozing damp of the dug-out's floor and walls ; but each was looking ahead and painting pictures conjured up by the man who had been in hospital—pictures of cosy, warm, brightly-lit compartments in the hospital train, of big cheerful hospital wards, with floors swept and polished to shining cleanliness, tables set out with bowls of bright-coloured flowers, beds sweet and fresh and clean, snow-white to the eye, down-soft to the touch, beds of an unspeakable and deeply longed-for comfort "with sheets" as the ex-casualty had put it, "that smooth and silky that when I thinks of rubbin' my chin an' wrigglin' my bare toes an' fingers on 'em, I fair purrs like a stroked kitten."

The silence was broken by the huskily whispered request of a man on a stretcher for "a mouthful o' water—just a mouthful." The orderly moistened the dry lips with some doubtful-looking water from a tin cup, but refused firmly to give the begged-for "mouthful."

"Shot through the stummick he is," the R.A.M.C. man explained to the others, "an' we've strick orders to give no drinks to shot stummicks. Don't none o' you go givin' 'im a drink when I'm not 'ere."

An R.A.M.C. sergeant groped his way down the dark steps, informed the dug-out that the order was to move along, and proceeded to apportion the stretchers and make all ready.

"The shellin' 'as gone over a bit," he said, "so we'd better get a move on an' get away before it comes on again."

"Oh, well," said he of the shell-smashed shoulder contentedly, "we're done wi' shellin' in an hour or two now. An' done with it for good, some o' us."

"The shellin', and the wet an' muck an' lousiness an' all, thank 'Eaven," said another man with two shattered legs, and "Thank Heaven!" several others echoed fervently.

All appeared to overlook or be indifferent to the fact that being done with these things "for ever" could only be because they were too crippled for further service—were, in fact, crippled for life.

They were carried up and laid out in the open with the cold rain beating on their faces until all were ready, the "shot stummick" lying with mouth wide open to catch the tiny drops.

"Now then, me lad," said the next-door stretcher case, "if that orderly sees you drinkin' the rain 'e'll 'ave to go'n turn it off at the tap."

"All ready there," called the sergeant, when all were out.

19

" All ready," and " Roll on Blighty," came the answer. " Pick up your kits—fall in—'Tchun ! Slo-o-ope arms," called another in imitation of the march parade orders, " Quick march ! " The pain-racked line giggled cheerfully and commenced to move off slowly and stumblingly.

Half a dozen bullets whistled shrilly over and a couple slapped into the wet ground close by. A group of shells wailed and howled past overhead and burst noisily over the ground towards which the men were moving ; the whole horizon ahead of them winked and blinked where the gun flashes beyond the crest lit the sky ; the drumming rifle fire and exploding grenades still shook the air behind them ; their feet slipped and slid on the greasy ground, jolting the laden stretchers and jarring and straining the stiffening wounds ; their nostrils were filled with the reek of cordite and high-explosive, of unburied dead and chloride of lime. Every sense was steeped in sight, sound, and stench of the battle-field, every nerve was a-quiver with pain or fatigue, and every step they moved was taken slowly and knowingly under the constant shadow of death.

Yet, great and terrible as all these things were, they were overborne by a greater thought, a wonderful content—the thought in the minds of each that he had " done his bit " plainly and to the proof of broken body and limb ; a content that sprang from the certainty to come of all the mental and bodily ease and comfort, the constant care and attention, the skill, the devotion, the kindness that to the firing line is all and always summed up in the two words or the symbol of the Red Cross.

It was a full three hours later and pitch dark when the squad, soaking wet and bone weary, jolted and racked and wrenched with pain, stumbled out on to the road down which the motor ambulances waited.

" Who goes there ? " a sentry challenged.

" We're the blinkin' Prussian Guards," answered the lad with the smashed shoulder swaying as he stood.

" We're the Blighty Squad," called another cheerfully. " Where's our bloomin' motor ? "

" Please, constable," mimicked the Cockney rifleman, " is this where Number Eleven General passes, and will it take me right to the Strand ? "

" Come on," called back the R.A.M.C. sergeant, who had moved on to speak to the sentry. " The motors are just down the road."

" Forward the Blighty Squad," came the answer, and the men squelched wearily on again.

" We won't be 'ome till mornin'," sang a voice.

The squad laughed.

BOYD CABLE.

MEN'S WEAR.

August. February.

" Dress does make a difference."

SERGT. J. H. THORPE, Artist Rifles.

THOSE WHO <u>SHOULD</u> WRITE ABOUT IT!

THOSE WHO <u>DO</u> WRITE ABOUT IT!

ENCYCLOPÆDIA OF MILITARY TERMS

ATTENTION (pronounced "Shun").—This is one of the most wonderful words in the military language. It is never spoken or whispered, it is always shouted, bellowed, shrieked, or screamed. Just according to the lung power of the officer or N.C.O. in charge of the squad or party which is to be drilled, paraded, fed, "clinked," washed, or (occasionally) paid. The effects of the command "Shun" on a battalion is both electrical and hypnotic. It is probably the only magic word now in use that was used in the days of Aladdin and his lamp. Should a poker game be in progress and the fabulous stakes be piled chin high on the dug-out or hut floor, until the scene resembles Monte Carlo or Dawson City, and an officer appears, some one utters the magic word "Shun," and the dug-out is immediately transformed into a Sister Susie sewing class, not a nickel or an ace can be seen. The officer usually says "Carry on," and out come chess boards, Psalm books, knitting needles, woodbines, mouth organs, writing material, girls' photographs, *The Listening Post*, and gingerbeer. "What did you say, Editor? Get on with the 'cyclopædia. Very good, Sir." Sir Robert Ball and the *Vancouver Sun* say that if Halley's Comet comes within one million miles of this earth, everything will be as quiet as the "German Navy." We're taking some awful chances when we say it, but the word "Shun" when a General or Colonel is on parade has got Halley's Comet beat fifty different ways as a silencer.—From *The Listening Post*.

"Shun."

At the Cross Roads

by "Platoon Commander"

THERE is a stretch of road, well known to those across the water, that runs somewhere between La Bassée and Bethune. At a certain point this road ceases to exist as a thing of use to man ; it has been blasted to bits by shells, and no man could live long who tried to thread his way from one shell crater to another. Here, on either side of the road, the British lie in their trenches facing their foes a few score yards away. At the other end, nearing Bethune, the road assumes its normal aspect ; motor cars, carts, wagons, and all war's ceaseless tide of traffic flow up and down. At yet another point, somewhere midway between the two towns named, the road is crossed by another running parallel to the British front. These cross roads form a very vital part of the British machinery for war. Down the two roads comes a constant stream of orderlies, messengers, staff officers, generals, ammunition trains, transport and supply columns, bodies of infantry, artillery, Red Cross wagons, details and detachments of all sorts and kinds. There is a little *estaminet* there which, like the widow's cruse, seems never to run dry of wine, and coffee, and rough cognac. All who can go in to have a drink, and in the partition reserved for officers much news of the war might be gathered by any one who had time to spend a day there and talk with those who passed.

Made in the Trenches

Second-Lieutenant Peter Henry Binks used to spend most of his day there; it was pleasanter than sitting on the triangle of worn turf in the centre of the cross roads where his examining picket lived. His sergeant would always come in and tell him if any civilians or suspicious persons were approaching, and then he could go out and examine them. But as a rule it was only troops and more troops that passed, and there was no need to examine them. Especially during the last two days had troops been passing incessantly. There was something very important stirring, that was certain, and even to Binks there filtered through the rumour that the British were on the eve of their big advance. Obviously at such a point as the cross roads it was of vital importance to see that none but friends went by; hence the examining picket.

Marching troops, as has been said, Binks let by, but one of his strictest orders was that he must stop every motor car, even if it held the Commander-in-Chief, and satisfy himself as to the *bona fide* of every occupant.

Binks was sitting on one chair with his feet on another, thinking of nothing in particular and sipping a little cognac and coffee when his sergeant entered and saluted.

"Motor car approaching, sir."

"Stop it," said Binks.

"Very good, sir," said the sergeant.

Binks rose, adjusted his belt, puffed himself out with an air of importance, and followed the sergeant into the road.

"Another Rolls-Royce," said Binks to himself; "luxurious dogs—the staff."

He approached the car and saluted the occupants—a major on the staff and another in khaki wearing the badge of a King's Messenger. Binks did not know the King's Messenger badge, and thought the latter was probably an ornament of the cavalry.

"Mornin'," said the major on the staff.

"Good morning, sir," said Binks.

"This is the —— cross roads, isn't it?" said the staff major.

"Yes, sir," said Binks.

"This is where we get out," said the staff major to his

companion. "Sir John said he would be along as soon as he could."

The two got down out of their car, directed the chauffeur to draw up by the side of the road, and turned towards the *estaminet*. Binks thought he ought to explain why he had stopped their car.

"I am in command of the examining post, sir," he said apologetically.

"That's all right, young fellow," said the major; "we were stopping here in any case. This is Captain Gort— the King's Messenger. He has orders to meet Sir John French here to-day to collect despatches. Come in and have a drink."

Binks was impressed. He followed meekly into the *estaminet*. The three settled themselves round a deal table; coffee and cognac were brought, and Binks and the major were soon talking affably. Captain Gort spoke little. He was a slim, fair young man with a pale moustache. The major was thickset, with a closely cropped head. He had a slight affectation of speech, which Binks attributed to the customs of good society.

Binks was much struck by the dignity of his company, and entertained the two officers with accounts of the life of an examining picket at the cross roads. He told them of all the troops that had passed. The news of the rumour of the coming great advance was of course no news to them, and the major confirmed the rumour, telling Binks it was a fact. Captain Gort was much interested in hearing of all the different troops that had gone by, and from time to time made notes in a pocket-book about certain details of the composition of units of infantry and artillery which Binks was able to give him. They went to the door of the inn once or twice as fresh bodies were going by and examined the troops which passed.

About one o'clock the two officers looked at their watches, and as the Commander-in-Chief had not come decided that he must be waiting for them elsewhere. They sent for their car, and, bidding Binks good-bye, went off.

27

Quarter of an hour after they had gone Binks' sergeant reported the approach of a second car. Binks stopped it, saluted, and asked the business of the occupants.

"King's Messenger," said one of the officers, muffled to the eyes in the flaps of his greatcoat.

Binks placed himself firmly in front of the car. This would not do at all. He called up his picket and requested the occupants to alight.

The man who had spoken expostulated. He said that he was in a great hurry and carried important despatches. He turned down the flap of his overcoat and showed Binks his badge.

Binks was immovable. He said that the King's Messenger had just gone by, and that the two fresh arrivals must consider themselves detained pending inquiries. The man who claimed to be the King's Messenger pricked up his ears on hearing of another who had preceded him, and begged Binks, whatever else he did, to telephone down the line to the next point which the first car must pass, have it stopped, and report that there was a second King's Messenger at the cross roads. This seemed reasonable to Binks, and having placed the two fresh arrivals in the charge of his escort he telephoned the message.

.   .   .   .   .   .

Meanwhile, the first car had gone on its way till it came to a second picket, where it was stopped.

At the second examining post the first King's Messenger and the major were stopped. They again were most affable, looked at their watches, and said they were waiting for Sir John French.

The subaltern was puzzled; the two officers spoke perfect English. There must be a mistake somewhere.

He explained that he had just received a telephone message from the officer commanding the examining picket at the cross roads to the effect that he had detained two officers who said they were meeting Sir John French by appointment, and one of whom claimed to be the King's Messenger.

At the Cross Roads

"Ah—so," said Captain Gort excitedly, "the other man who says he is the King's Messenger a lie tells."

It was a little slip to have made—just that verb at the end of the sentence—but the staff major knew it was all up and looked at Captain Gort as though he could have killed him. Two days later he was spared the trouble, and shared the same fate himself.

"VE'RE DUN"
1916

ENCYCLOPÆDIA OF MILITARY TERMS

(*Continued*)

BARBED WIRE.—Some one has written that this was invented by Mephisto. After what we have heard about him it is surprising that he should invent anything of such an affectionate and "clinging" nature. At the front it is used for giving an artistic finish to a trench. No trench is complete without it. It is planted at night in order that the artillery may plough it up in the morning. A good crop of barbed wire has been known to prevent opposing armies from arguing the "point." When a soldier gets tangled up in it he says things which are not taught at school. This may be the reason why the Padre never goes on a wiring party or leads an attack.

BILLET.—On active service a billet may be anything from a shed to a château. Usually the former. When troops are to be moved from one part of the front to another, a billeting party is sent in advance. These men receive explicit instructions to locate the most draughty and leaky barns in the country. At this they are experts. The generous-hearted farmers then inform their cattle and pigs that they must be very polite and wipe their feet before walking over a brave soldier's blankets. He also gives the hens and chickens warning not to lay eggs where a soldier may crush them. The farmer's wife then pours a jug of beer into a barrel of water, his daughters practise a "No compres" smile and everything is ready for the reception of the "Soldat Canadien."—From *The Listening Post.*

The Clutching Hand.

THE MAKING OF MICKY McGHEE

By R. W. CAMPBELL,

Author of "Private Spud Tamson," etc.

MICKY McGHEE enlisted for ale, for sleep,
and for bread,
To carry the kilt and doublet, the glen-
garry on his head.
He was not what men call handsome, his form was rather
spent,
And his hair was thin, his nose was stumped, and his eyes
of cute intent.
He'd been used to sleeping in " Models," used to sleeping in
gaols ;
Drinking the stuff that burneth, and courting the women
called " Tails."
Hunger, sorrow, and sickness were all his eyes had seen ;
Hope was not in his keeping. He wasn't a might-have-been.

Life had made him a rebel. He was a nomad from smelling
slums,
Who'd only come for drink and bread, and not for the soul
of the drums,

NOTE.—Reprinted by special permission from "The Making of Micky McGhee and other Poems," George Allen & Unwin, Ltd., 3s. 6d. net.

31

Made in the Trenches

Yet he flung his vermined "civvies" off with a shout of joy,
And let a Sergeant scrub away the filth of a strange alloy.
Then he dressed in an ancient Tartan; marched to the barrack-
room
To learn the valour of heroes, the glory there is in doom,
And how the sons of Princes and Peers are pals of men like he,
Sharing with manly pleasure the skirmish, the march, and the
spree.

The road was rough and brimful of orders that brook no
delay—
It wasn't all beer and skittles to serve for a "bob" a day;
Réveillé ended his blanket dreams; Corporals called, "Show
a leg,
Out of that now, you, Micky McGhee, or I'll put 'on the
peg.'"
He was made to wash his teeth and neck—things he didn't
know,
Made to brush his hair in "quiffs," crease his trews like a beau,
Cursed when he wore his cap at meals and fingered the spuds
and stew,
"Pegged" every time he answered, "What the h—'s that tae
dae wi' you?"

"Come along now, you, Private McGhee," said the old In-
structor at drill;
"You waddle along like a navvy that's had a pint and a gill.
Step up, step up, now, Micky. Hold up your head and eyes,
Straighten your legs like a soldier. Damn it, man, look your
size!
I've trained Ghurkas and Sepoys, Keelies and burglars too;
I'll have none of your shuffling, I'll make you a soldier true.
Halt, there! Halt!" roared the Sergeant. "What was that
you said?"
"Tae h— wi' you!" roared Micky, striking him on the head.

So Micky McGhee was sentenced to twenty-eight days in the
cells,

The Making of Micky McGhee

Where he thought, as he picked his oakum, of "Models" and
    frowsy belles,
And of one by the name of Sarah, who'd often given him a
    " chew,"
A chunk of her pauper rations, a drink of the cheapest
    brew.
Would he go back to Sarah, the " Model," and things of sin ?
These were the thoughts that sent his head into a swirling
    din.
Then the good that's in the vilest whispered, " No, lad, stick out ;
The Army is kind to the sin-
    ner, and the men that the
    merchants clout."

Now the ways of the weak are
    guided, not by their holy
    vows,
But the seeds of sin that's in
    their souls—seeds for crime
    and rows,
And the thirst that is eternal in
    a man of Micky's kind
Is caused through the breed of
    hunger, sorrow, and sickened
    mind.
The God who's the God of all
    men can pity the mood
    when he
Craved for the liquor that burn-
    eth on the day that he
    was free ;
Pint and pint he called for, till
    drunk he lurched once
    again
Into the Quarter Guard Room,
    his vows all rent in
    twain.

Micky McGhee.

C

For this he was marched under escort, in front of a Captain
   and Lord,
Son of a Duke and a " White Man," and known to his men
   as " Bob."
Said he, " McGhee, I am sorry you've been a fool once again ;
Still, I feel there's good in all of you rough and tumble men.
Now, McGhee, let's make a bargain. If I let you off this
   time,
Will you play the game like a sportsman—keep out of drink
   and crime ?
Come ! On your word of honour—you're going to play the
   game !"
"Yes, Sir," said Micky, the sinner, his heart in a righteous
   flame.

But the battle was stiff and uppish : he was fighting the sins
   of sires,
And the craving for drink was hellish—like raging passions' fires,
And his nomad spirit suffered, for he'd the love of the road,
While the craving for Sarah's comforts piled on another load.
Yet, the spirit of God that's in all men whispered, " Micky,
   stick out."
The kindly rule of the Duke's son kept off the Non-Com.'s
   clout.
And *then* came the Ultimatum—War and freedom from lures,
An outlet for hidden glories ; the chance that murders or cures.

Thus the son of a Peer and a Pauper, linked in the cause
   that's high,
Marched in the march of glory ; suffered, and asked not why.
At Mons when hell from the cannon staggered, slaughtered,
   and maimed,
When wave upon wave of Germans charged for the gods
   they claimed,
Micky, grim-jawed and eager, fired with that aim of Hythe,
Which mows the living to slaughter like the sweep of a
   Terror-Scythe,

34

The Making of Micky McGhee

Tho' left to cover the Great " Retreat," flanked, then surrounded with foes,
The son of the Peer and Pauper fought, and wailed not their
woes.

Britain, you've had noble glories, but none so great as that
day
When fifty-five of the Highland host were caught by the
Huns' foray.
Their rounds were fired, and vanished; all that was left was
the steel,
As they rose with a cheer and plunged it home into the
swine who squeal.
Gad ! what a noble ending—plunging, then warding the blows,
Smashing heads with their butt-ends, ripping the hearts of their
foes.
But the horde seemed never-ending, and circled like vultures
low,
Bent on the mad destruction of " Bob " & Micky & Co.

" We're done, men. Scatter and go — make for the rear —
retire,"
Roared " Bob " as he fell dying at the feet of his slum esquire.
With a rage of a frenzied lover Micky laid two more low,
Then flinging away his rifle, lifted his Captain to go
To the rear for succour and safety, for him he loved so well.
But, alas ! the steel of a German ended his life. He fell
Dead by the side of his Captain. Thus the Peer and Pauper
died,
Linked in the sleep of glory—the death that's an Empire's
pride.

.   .   .   .   .

Made in the Trenches

There's a woman that lives in " Models "; known as Sarah to all—
A broken soul of the scourings, that environment throws to
    the wall ;
Yet she, like the Fairies of Joyland, has her dreams of the
    past as well ;
'Tis the dream of the man called Micky—Micky, the man who
    fell.
And her pride is a silver medal, a letter and statement of pay
From the man who cherished her dearly, and saved on a " bob "
    a day
Ten pounds to this woman called Sarah—crude, yet kind as a
    dove,
Whose charity in the mean streets gained her a soldier's love.

" Model " means a common lodging-house.

36

—AND THEN THEY CHARGED US!

Sergeant-Major: "You isolated men will not bathe with the others. I'm 'aving part of the river put on one side for you."

THE OASIS

AFRICA

FOR eight weary days we had crawled across the burning desert. In all directions stretched the wastes of the mighty Sahara. Sand, sand, and always sand ; hills of sand, valleys of sand, and paths of sand. Sand in the scanty food, sand in the brackish water—water that was drunk lukewarm from a clammy, loathsome water-skin. Sand in one's mouth, nose, and eyes. . . . Misery of hunger, torture of thirst ; unending discomfort of swarming lice. Footsore and weary, but ever before us the pointing finger of the Arab Sheikh, and his ceaseless : " On, on."

We had started the journey poorly equipped, and now, having lost two precious days on the way, it seemed likely that if we did not soon strike the oasis, the caravan would perish of thirst. Clutch tight your water-skin on the desert, for there is no charity on the Sahara, and he that has no water shall not drink !

One day the dreaded sirocco had swept upon us. Wrapped in our flowing blankets, we had crouched low beside the kneeling camels while the fiery sand-storm passed over. Sweating in the heat, we had lost the whole day, dreading to be buried alive in the drifting sand. This danger past, we had lost another day making a wide detour to the east in order to avoid the fierce, tameless Tuaregs, who were marauding in the district. This was a day when fear laid his hand upon us, when each of us felt the knife at his throat. But the Sheikh's skilful leading saved us, and, taking the caravan through some deep sandy defiles, we passed the raiding party without being seen. Later we heard that Sheikh Abdulla had fallen upon the bandits, and the tale of his vengeance

is still told in hushed whispers in all the bazaars of Tripolitana—
from the secret city of the Senussi to the unveiled walls of
Ghadames the Mysterious.

I was at the end of my tether, racked with fever and aching
all over ; the heavy, old-fashioned Mauser weighed me down
whilst a string of sores marked the place where the cartridge
bandolier galled my shoulders. I was uneasy in my mind, too.
The Arabs were clearly dejected at not having reached the oasis,
and several had already commenced to feel the pangs of thirst. I
fancied they looked at me with envious eye as I occasionally
gulped down a mouthful of water from my skin. A well-struck
blow and the water-skin would be theirs. Besides, the infidel was
known to carry money, a sum that camp-fire talk had inflated to
large proportions.

After a short halt, under the blazing sun, the Sheikh again
gave the order to advance. On, on ! I struggled up, but my
leaden feet almost refused to bear me.

"Mohammed ! " I called to my faithful Algerian, "I can do
no more ; I am done ! "

"Courage, Effendi, courage ! " he answered, looking genuinely
distressed at my condition. "Still a little way and we shall sight
the oasis. Risk not our lives by lingering in this evil place."

"Our lives, Mohammed ? " I queried.

The Arab drew himself up.

"Does the Effendi think I would desert him in his hour
of need ? But God is good, let us press on."

I took a good drink and lurched forward. I shambled along
with clouded brain, but every fibre of my body torn with pain
and fatigue. On, on !

Suddenly the Sheikh stopped and pointed to the south. The
caravan halted, and every one prepared his arm. Matchlocks
were primed, cartridges rammed home, and swords loosened in
their sheaths. Was it the Tuaregs again across our path ? But
Mohammed, the keen-eyed, shouted joyfully—

"The oasis, the oasis ! I see the palm-trees."

The Arabs burst into a loud shout of "Thank God ! " and
with my glasses I could just pick out the tiny patch of green
dancing in the hot air. In a short time we were on the fringe
of one of the most delicious spots I have ever seen.

The Oasis

The oasis was set in the sand of the desert like an emerald on a shield of gold. The massive green foliage of the graceful palms was delightfully welcome to eyes smarting and sore with the glare of the eternal sand. How delightful it was to sit in the shade of a moss-grown bank, while at one's feet a brook ran babbling, picking its way through the cultivated patches! There it splashed noisily into a clear, round pond, and what pleasure could the gods have given greater than the luxurious bath I enjoyed in it. Then the cool and shady tent and the banquet prepared by Mohammed, with the lavish presents the Sheikh of the place had sent to me. And above all was the sense of peace and safety; that here, at all events, one could lay down to rest without having to snatch up revolver and rifle at every noise.

Now that the sun has set, look for a moment at the pageant of the heavens, framed by the open end of the tent. Like a filmy scarf of silver, the Milky Way lay on the dusky bosom of the sky. The beauty of the night was jewelled with the brightest stars that charm the heart of man. Canopus, the great star of prehistoric Egypt, blazed white above the horizon; Sirius shone like a peerless diamond, and Aldeberan like a ruby. Slowly and solemnly the tail of the Great Bear swept round the Pole, like the hand of a mighty timepiece, majestic enough to tell off the hours of Eternity. . . .

Lulled by the soft music of the brook, in infinite content, I sank back on to the soft carpets, and was soon in a dreamless slumber.

EUROPE

All night long the battalion had shivered in the assembly trenches; for, in view of the attack that was to be made shortly after dawn, blankets had been left behind in order to lighten the men's packs. The sun shot up bright and comforting. Its appearance was hailed with delight by the soldiers, although— solemn thought—the breaking of day was the death-signal for many of those who now lay about in the full pride of their manhood.

A motor-cycle spurted along the adjacent road. The Colonel

took the message, threw away his cigarette, and gave the signal to advance into the support trenches. Belts were tightened, packs adjusted, and the battalion cleared the intervening field at the double. The preliminary bombardment had now started, and the air was torn with the shuffle and hiss of shells fired by the British guns. Almost at once the enemy woke up, and his artillery took up the challenge. They guessed at the position of the English supports, and guessed well; had the battalion not been in well-constructed trenches, the accurately timed shrapnel would have taken a heavy toll. Even as it was, the Regimental Medical Officer had plenty to do, and he passed from trench to trench bandaging the wounded and directing their removal to the rear.

The Surgeon was seized with a strange exhilaration; he seemed to have lived for this day. He had wandered the whole world over with pride and thankfulness in his heart that he could call himself an Englishman, and now an opportunity was given him to risk his life in the service of his country. And to risk it in such good company too; to go into action with one of the most famous regiments of the line—that was an honour he had never dreamt of, even in the wildest flights of imagination.

The noise and din became greater and greater. Shrapnel burst viciously through the trees and the ground quaked with the thud of the high-explosive shells. Machine-guns rapped out death monotonously, and the air was filled with the singing of rifle bullets.

Between the trenches a soldier lay with his arm shattered by a shrapnel bullet. Kneeling beside him, the Surgeon rapidly slit up the sleeve and plugged the spurting artery with his thumb. With his free hand he was searching in his haversack for a tourniquet, when he was conscious of a resounding crash and something hot was dashed in his face. Every pulse in his body throbbed violently and he was deafened by a loud ringing in his ears. His left arm dropped useless to his side; a stinging, stabbing pain raged along it. But this seemed nothing to the fear of the black mist that veiled his eyes. He rubbed away a sticky mass, and a great joy surged over him when he knew his vision was unharmed. He looked at the wounded soldier and saw that medical skill could do no more for him. A large fragment of the bursting shell had struck him on the head and his blood had splashed into the Surgeon's face. The latter looked at his own arm. He was appalled at the sight of the white bone sticking from the wound and the steady drip, drip of the blood. He felt vanquished and humiliated; uncontrollable tears gushed from his eyes. He had set out to do great things, and this was the end! He shambled into the trench and called querulously for a stretcher-bearer. Although usually able to stand a shelling with fair composure, he was now seized with fear, and he crouched apprehensively at the bottom of the trench. Soon his arm was roughly bandaged, and he commenced the painful journey to the Dressing Station. There he drank thirstily at a water-bottle and lay down to wait for the ambulance. The next day was a nightmare of moving and jolting. He changed from horse-ambulance to motor-car, from hospital train to steamboat. On the journey the wound inflamed, and the limb became swollen. As the fever mounted, imagination took wider and more pessi-mistic sweeps. Mental suffering was added to physical; the worst was feared and pondered upon. Death itself did not appear so terrible; one had walked side by side with it for months. But to be maimed, to be helpless, to be dependent on others. . . .

In London the car stopped outside a large house. A flood of light poured out as the door was opened and the Surgeon saw framed there a group of devoted women, ready to help his stum-bling feet over the threshold, anxious to ease his sufferings. What a relief to get dirty and blood-stained clothes off, and how delicious to lie down between soft white linen sheets! But best of all, there was the gentle hand of a woman to smooth the pillow and the soft rustle of her skirts to banish the sense of fear and loneliness.

Ah, dear God, at last—the Oasis!

ERNEST H. GRIFFIN,
Capt. R.A.M.C.

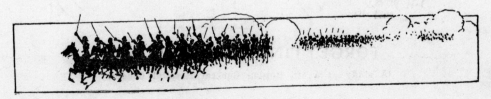

J.H.DOWD
MAY '16

FORGETTING THEIR PAINS

(A study at a 3rd Gordon General Hospital Concert.)

A LAMENT

I AM in hospital, and I have a grievance. A sad combination of circumstances, as you will agree.

Fortunately, my grievance is not against the hospital, which is, to quote the song, a little bit of heaven, peopled by angels in nurses' uniform. To tell the honest truth, I am rather afraid my trouble is imaginary, because when I look round the ward I find that all the other patients wear a rather peevish expression, which gives me the impression, probably only too near the truth, that I see different examples of my own reflections in a mirror.

Even visitors; and this brings me to my pathetic tale which I will now unfold.

People come to see me quite often and all of them make praiseworthy efforts to cheer me up and make me laugh. As my own particular trouble has given me, owing to the complicated dressings, a strong resemblance to a mumps case, laughter is a difficult and rather dangerous feat of endurance. The other day a friend of mine came in and sat down.

"Hallo, young man," he began cheerfully, "you look about as merry as the Chamber of Horrors on a wet Good-Friday. You want to buck up a bit. That reminds me, have you heard the yarn about the young subaltern in France who——"

I had heard the story before, and thought it rather a poor one; nevertheless after a protracted struggle my face slipped into a smile. "That's the best story I have heard for some time," I said; "I don't know where you lads pick them up."

After all, one must do one's bit to encourage visitors.

So far so good, but when he had gone, the rest of the ward began with one accord to ask for a repetition of the tale. "Must have been a good one to make *you* laugh, old man."

45

I did my best with it, and a strong vote of censure was immediately passed unanimously.

"Something of the same sort happened to my uncle during the Crimea," a Major in the corner murmured with heavy sarcasm.

Feeling thoroughly crushed I lay back in bed and turned my face to the wall.

I will not harrow your feelings by giving further details of that afternoon; rather let us draw a veil over my sorrows by saying that no less than seven times during the next three days was I told the same story, with variations, by different visitors.

After a time I came to expect the story as a matter of course, and felt bitterly disappointed if it was not told. I took an intense interest in the various ways different raconteurs led to it. I began to see points in it that I had failed to notice at first. The more I heard and thought of it the more I liked it. I grew to look upon it as a friend.

One morning, after a sleepless night, I decided to tell it myself. That day my father came to see me. I don't know if I can tell you this, but I fear my feelings toward him will never be quite the same. I carefully manœuvred the conversation round to subalterns.

"By the way," I said casually, "do you know the story about the subaltern who——" I told him the whole story, even adding little details of my own. *He never smiled.*

This was the beginning of the end. I was determined to have my little ewe lamb appreciated at its proper worth. I told it to every one I met, even the Doctor.

After a time I grew anxious. Could it be that I was wrong, or was it not as good a story as I believed? I persevered with it, I told it in every possible way. I even tried giving away the point at the beginning. Alas, a failure! Whenever I start it now people say, "Oh, yes, I know that one, but do *you* know the story about——"

I have exhausted the possibilities of all my friends, and I fear the little tale must die the lonely death of the unappreciated.

A Lament

But stay, there is one more chance. Have *you* heard the story? No? Well, here it is. I warn you that you may never forget it.

A certain regiment was billeted in some farm buildings in Flanders, and a young subaltern was sitting in a despondent attitude in front of the kitchen stove. His company commander came in and asked him why the air of gloom.

"Well," said the sub., "I think I've overdrawn at Cox's, and I'm afraid they may stop my cheques. I don't know how to find out how my account stands."

"That's easy," was the reply; "write them."

The sub. looked doubtful. "I'm not much of a hand at writin'."

The Major laughed. "All you've got to do is to write an official letter asking after your balance. Imagine you are writing a report for the C.O. I'll go away and leave you by yourself to wrestle with it."

The sub. settled down with his pen, ink, and paper, as the French say. Three hours later the company commander looked in and found him in the same position, surrounded by piles of crumpled paper. He tiptoed and looked over his shoulder.

After three hours' brainwork, the sub. had written: "I say, Cox——"

"PETER."

❁   ❁   ❁

PUNCTUALITY!

Sergeant-Major : "Fall in here again at ELEVEN o'clock. When I say ELEVEN o'clock I don't mean five minutes past ELEVEN, I mean FIVE MINUTES TO.

(From *The Listening Post*.)

47

ENCYCLOPÆDIA OF MILITARY TERMS

(Continued)

DUG-OUT.—A hole in the ground with a lid on. There are three kinds of dug-outs at the front.

The " Bungalow " for Officers, the " Love in a Cottage " for Sergeants, and the " Noah's Ark " for privates. They are built for men, mice, rats, and cats to sleep in. A dug-out is decorated with jam, cheese, photographs, and fleas.

DAM.—This is what the Engineers do to a river or " Ford." By simply adding the letter " N " we have a suitable prefix for use when referring to the Kaiser, the weather, a heavy pack, a route march, a dirty rifle, a working party, a leaky dug-out, and barbed wire, etc. It is used unhesitatingly by all troops excepting the Padre, his nearest approach being " Darned."

DRESSING STATION.—The home of pills, poultices, plasters, cascarettes, castor oil, and catgut, needles, knives, and " nerves."

DEFAULTER.—A man who has made up his mind to be more careful " next time."

48

THE SENSITIVE PLANT

"It's their damned machinery!" said Halbury viciously. "We'd have cleared them out months ago on anything like equal terms, but you can't go scalp-hunting with those nasty boggle-eyed machine guns winking round every corner."

His companion spat in disgust. "I came to do soldiering," he muttered, "and am metamorphosed into an earth-worm. I haven't seen a German for ten weeks—beyond the blighter we dropped yesterday, sniping."

They sat back in the little dug-out and played their forty-seventh hand of "Nap" wearily.

"I'll go three," said Halbury.

His companion hesitated, then seized the top card of the pack.

"I'll try the lot," he retorted.

He played the hand and was beaten on the last card—the King of Spades.

"Well, I'm—well—did you ever——" Finding decent English inadequate, he burst into a torrent of swearing.

"Drop it!" said Halbury, in a low voice.

"Drop what?"

"Foul language."

"Good Heavens! it's part of the business. Time was

when I was a nice-mannered person in a quite respectable business house. I suppose that must have been about a hundred and fifty years ago. Since then I have learned the art of vocal expression as constructed for military usage. Everybody does it. Why, you're worse than any. I've heard——"

"One is influenced by circumstances," said Halbury simply.

"What do you mean?"

Halbury took the cigarette from his mouth and inclined his head towards the corner of the dug-out, in the faint light of which a figure lay prone in a sleeping attitude.

"Oh, Craig!"

"Yes; he doesn't like it."

"Has he had the cheek to say so?"

"No; I've happened to notice."

"H'm! He's a peculiar lot. I'm afraid he'll have to put up with it unless the army is willing to adopt an entirely new vocabulary—Pass! What a mouldy lot! Not a trick among them."

"He flung down the cards on to the improvised table and rose to his feet.

"Oh, God! I'm fed up with it all."

The figure in the corner stirred a little and then emerged from the brown army blanket.

"Who's 'fed up'?" he asked.

"I am," said the complainer, with a grunt; "fed up with all this wallowing in slime and filth; sick of the deadly monotony of it all. It isn't a war at all—it's an exhibition of patience. Why doesn't the old man let us go for them?"

"Kick the brute," said Halbury. "There's no method in his madness."

Craig smiled in a peculiar way. He was young, not more than twenty, but well set up, and with a face which while not handsome was nevertheless pleasant to look upon.

The nose was straight and rather prominent, and the eyes were set wide apart, evidencing breadth of view and a natural appreciation of life's best things.

"I think it's all very wonderful," he said softly.

"What's wonderful?"

50

" All this vast gathering of men, willing to fight and die for the things they hold dear."

" Rot !" said the iconoclast ; "they're in it for the fun of the thing."

" Yes," replied Craig, " but always with the consciousness that their action is justified by necessity."

" H'm—perhaps ; but how long are we going to stay here ? "

" Does it matter ? "

" Matter ? Good Heavens ! It's enough to drive one insane. The monotony—the dreadful sameness of the thing."

" Sameness ! There's no sameness in life," said Craig. " Every day adds a new chapter. Yesterday one evolved a new theory ; to-day one develops it ; to-morrow—why, to-morrow the whole world has changed."

" Throw something at him," said the other ; " he'll perhaps wake up then."

Craig took his tunic and cleaned the buttons vigorously. He was scrupulously clean, almost to the extent of fastidiousness. His mind took a retrospective survey of the last twelve months. For him indeed the whole world was changed, and was changing again and again day after day. He had yearned for life with an intensity immeasurable. Far away on the prairie, under the clear inscrutable heavens, he had sat and wondered at Life, Nature, and God. What did it all mean ? Motherless, fatherless, but with responsibilities upon his shoulders—two small sisters—he enlarged his small circle of life by a close understanding of God's handiwork.

His world stretched out in limitless spans of imagery and rested—where ? He never knew. And then came into his hands Browning, which complicated the enigma of existence in a strange fashion. It confused his theories, but it widened his mind, and out of the wild chaos of thought which rushed and murmured through his everyday life a few shreds of truth came incoherently but persistently. Like the Browning which he loved but only half understood, he was " full of the most intensest life," and when the call came he responded and felt the pulse of a fuller existence throb strongly in his being. Oh, life was wonderful indeed !

Made in the Trenches

One morning in early spring D Company moved up to the little wood and Craig went with it. It was pleasanter here, for the trees and young shrubs were shooting into life with a clean greenness which was in pleasant contrast with the smashed and lacerated ground round about the trenches in open country. True, the outer fringe of the wood was torn to shreds with the constant hails and shells and machine-gun fire, but in the second line of trenches which D Company occupied life ran a smooth, even course, and save for an occasional shell and a few stray singing bullets one might have been in one of the delicious green confines which abound in Surrey and Kent.

In less than a month the little wood was completely transformed. Paths were made in every direction, neat little bridges were put across streams, and sign-posts abounded everywhere. "Regent Street" ran at right angles to "Oxford Street," and Piccadilly constituted the main thoroughfare into which all paths converged. Climbing a high tree, Craig saw the British first line go twisting snake-wise far up into the north almost exactly parallel with the enemy's first line, save in one place where a great farm-house formed the bone of contention between both belligerents.

"They're at it again, Halbury," said Craig. "I wonder who's got it now."

"It hardly matters," replied Halbury. "It changes hands daily. It's nothing less than a charnel-house."

All through the winter the fight for the lone farm had gone on. No sooner did the enemy take it than they were driven out pell-mell at the point of the bayonet, and then the process was reversed, and so on until whole companies withered away. And yet neither side would give in, and each day found a new affray bloodier than the former. When the occupants were vanquished and expelled their artillery would smother it with shells, until after thirty-five of these ferocious minor episodes hardly one stone remained upon another; but it still remained the coveted possession of either side.

"Craig," said Halbury one morning, "there's a bundle of books for our company. Come and scramble for 'em."

Craig walked languidly to where the corporal was unpacking

"Came upon a great toad with magnificent jewel-like eyes."

a bulky parcel. In a little dell behind the trench two white daffodils had opened during the night. He looked at them interestedly. Near by a few violets were straining to bend their heads and a primrose had already yielded to the sun. He knelt down and cut away some fibrous weed from the roots of the violets and came upon a great toad with magnificent jewel-like eyes. It seemed strange to him that Nature should work in her quiet, miraculous manner when death was stalking over the land; and when he tried to work it all out he found himself in front of a vast problem altogether too large for him.

"God works in a mysterious fashion," he murmured; and that was as far as he got.

Then he suddenly remembered the books, and arrived to find them all distributed save one small dilapidated volume which he pocketed without looking at it.

In the evening by candle-light he took it from his pocket and turned over the pages. It was Shelley's "Sensitive Plant." He commenced to read.

> A Sensitive Plant in a garden grew,
> And the young winds fed it with silver dew,
> And it opened its fan-like leaves to the light,
> And closed them beneath the kisses of night.

It was his first acquaintance with Shelley; hitherto he had been but a name. He read on and on, and as he read so the incomparable music of the thing reverberated throughout his being.

> For the Sensitive Plant has no bright flower;
> Radiance and odour are not its dower;
> It loves, even like Love, its deep heart is full,
> It desires what it has not, the Beautiful!

The candle guttered and burned low, but still he read, and never had he known such delight. Halbury came in from Guard and flung himself down dog-tired, but the figure beside the candle, prone, with chin on hands, still wandered in a world of imagery, picturing in its fullest detail "The Lady, the wonder of her kind" who "Tended the garden from morn to even," and when he reached the end he turned again to the beginning, and, disregarding the music, read it in its fuller meaning, and so came to him a whole flood of new truths. There seemed to be no sleep that night—it was like a magic transportation to a sublunar heaven where time and space are not, where dreams are made whole and thoughts materialized. And through it all the key to its being sobbed and murmured in his brain—

> That garden sweet, that lady fair,
> And all sweet shapes and odours there
> In truth have never passed away;
> 'Tis we, 'tis ours, are changed; not they.

Day followed day with a sameness of detail that drove men to despair. Anything in the nature of a fight would have been a godsend. But Craig moved in his little world happy and content. The Sensitive Plant was to him a real thing; had not the poet himself written—

> For love, and beauty, and delight,
> There is no death nor change: their might
> Exceeds our organs, which endure
> No light, being themselves obscure.

And was it not even here in this little wood, this " no man's land " ? Might not this patch of green be the same garden, and she, " The wonder of her kind," even now tending the flowers ? Was she and her garden any more visionary than these guns and sandbags, wire and rifles ? Might they not be the dream and she the reality ? And then in the midst of this fond hypothesis there came a great and obsessing idea. The more he thought on it the more it entranced him.

" Halbury," he said quietly one morning, " you have friends in England ; will you get some seeds for me ? "

" Great Scott ! " ejaculated the latter, " what on earth do you want seeds for ? "

" To plant."

" Where ? "

" Here—behind the trench."

" But—but seeds don't grow in a night ? "

" Well——? "

" Well, one of these days we're going forward."

" How does that affect it ? "

" Well, your seeds would be wasted."

" They could never be wasted if they came up."

" But some other fellow would collar the flowers."

" Well," with a smile, " that wouldn't matter, would it ? "

" H'm ! I suppose not ! "

" Then you'll get them ? "

" Of course ; what do you want ? "

Craig gave him a written list. Roses, Snowdrops, Violets, Tulips, Narcissi, Lilies, Hyacinths, Jessamine, Sensitive Plant.

Halbury read through the list.

" Good Heavens ! You're too late. These things should be planted months ago. Never mind, I'll get young plants in the mould and you can transplant them. But what's this *Sensitive Plant* ?—never heard of it."

" But it exists."

" Does it ? Never mind, I'll ask for it."

The list was posted, and Craig waited in an agony of suspense.

At last the plants arrived. The boxes were opened, and Craig feasted his eyes on the green treasures. D Company looked on in amazement. " What does he want with those things ? " said the iconoclast. " Why doesn't he put up a greenhouse and grow tomatoes and cucumbers ? I could just manage a nice cucumber."

Craig was looking through the plants, checking them against the list ; as he came to the end he looked at Halbury in despair.

" It hasn't come."

" What hasn't ? "

" The Sensitive Plant."

" I didn't think it would. I don't believe there is such a thing."

" But there *is*," said Craig persistently.

" Well, never mind," said Halbury. " I'll write to a florist I know."

He wrote, but no reply ever came.

In the meantime Craig had mapped out his Shelleyian garden. D Company watched the operation with interest and with considerably diminishing scorn. It was easy to smile and joke when the thing was merely an idea, but when the garden became a reality and the scent and odour of the flowers blew into their nostrils each morning the ignominy and embarrassment was theirs. The thing became contagious. Each man marked out a little plot as his own and transplanted wild flowers from the recesses of the wood. But Craig's garden remained the sole horticultural topic of the day. It grew magically from a bare patch of brown earth to a glorious living thing. Every spare moment of Craig's time found him busily employed watering and weeding, and applying deft touches here and there.

The Colonel and the Major came and congratulated the owner, but Craig smiled a wan smile and strove to subdue the heartache within him. As the Colonel was leaving Craig stammered out the question which was ever in his heart.

"Oh, sir! can you tell me where to get a 'Sensitive Plant'?"

The Colonel twisted his monocle fiercely.

"Never heard of the thing, my man; never heard of it— except in Shelley."

"Yes—yes, that's it," said Craig eagerly.

"H'm—never seen one. I'll see what we can do."

Craig lived on the pinnacle of hope for two weeks, then sank into the depths of remorse. Neither the Colonel nor the Major nor any of their friends had ever seen such a thing.

The summer advanced and the garden grew in splendour and colour.

> And the jessamine faint, and the sweet tuberose,
> The sweetest flower for scent that blows;
> And all rare blossoms from every clime
> Grew in that garden in perfect prime."

But Craig remained inconsolable, and when the evening breeze wafted the odour of the roses into his trench, it but added to his misery and brought tears of mortification to his eyes. It was but a garden such as one might see in a thousand English villages; it could never be what he would have it to be—the materialization of a wonderful conception —how could it be, with the reigning spirit absent?

"Craig," said Halbury one evening, "I'm told off with some others to clear those German snipers out of the farm-house. They've got a machine gun there and are playing the devil with our outposts."

He shook hands and went off.

For two days Craig saw no more of him ; and then, late at night, there was heavy firing on their left wing, and a flood of men retired into the wood. Halbury was amongst them, his arm in a rough sling.

"Devil of a time," he confided. "We cleared the farm-house and then the whole German line broke loose. They've shoved our line back two hundred yards, and we only saved envelopment by coming here. Oh, you ought to have seen the farm-house—a regular wreck. There was a fine conser-vatory, filled from top to bottom with plants all ruined and dead. Only one thing was untouched. I was just going to sneak it when the beggars came down on us. A funny plant too, with quaint leaves. I went to touch one of them and it curled up as though it resented my interference."

Craig suddenly started.

"What was it like?" he asked eagerly.

"Oh, I don't know ; about two feet high—no bloom."

"And the leaves—the leaves?"

"Very peculiar—like fans."

Craig walked up and down in great agitation.

"Ah, Halbury, that was it—that was it."

"That was what?"

"Why, the Sensitive Plant."

Halbury uttered a low whistle. "Well," he rejoined, "it might as well be in Jericho. There's no earthly chance of getting it now."

Craig sat and moped, and Halbury went into hospital to get his wound dressed.

The next day was spent in burying those that fell in the fighting. They were interred decently and respectfully—not in groups, but singly, in the rear corner of the wood. Above each little mound of earth a neat wooden cross was placed. Craig returned to his trench muddy and weary and not a little upset by the grim reality of it all.

In the evening all was quiet save for the low rumble of distant artillery and the quick flash of the guns over the horizon. Craig was deep in the well-worn little volume of Shelley. For the hundredth time he chanted the wonderful lines under his breath, and for the hundredth time was filled with the same gnawing desire for the plant which he pitied and loved beyond everything else. When the night was far advanced he took his rifle, slung it across his shoulder, and crawled out of the trench.

It was terribly dark, and he ran into trees and almost ricked his ankle many times among the rabbit-warrens and twisted roots, but eventually he cleared the wood and found himself outside the first lines. Once in the open the " going " was much easier, but the risk of detection infinitely greater.

A German sentry challenged him. He dived into a shell crater and waited half an hour in dreadful suspense. Then he moved forward again painfully and slowly. The farm-house lay in an acre of garden, circumscribed by a stone wall, now but a mass of broken rubbish. He climbed over and made his way across the morass which once was devoted to intensive culture. Weeds and decaying vegetation clung round his legs, filling his nostrils with a strange new stench. He thought instinctively of the last pages of " The Sensitive Plant." How strangely it all fitted in ! He found the conservatory at the back of the house, every pane of its glass broken to atoms. Softly he crept through a huge shell-hole in the side of it and waited a few moments. From an adjacent room the low murmur of German voices could be heard. He hesitated, then drew a box of matches from his pocket. He was about to strike one when he heard the measured tread of a sentry outside. He crouched beneath the frame of a large stand and held his breath. The footsteps gradually diminished into silence. Then he struck a match, shielding its flame with both hands. Quickly he groped around the place, evading the broken earthenware scattered over the floor. Everything was dead and decaying. Rare plants whose names he knew not lay twisted and rotting. Somehow it seemed more terrible than the battlefield itself. Desolation was complete. Eventually he found what he sought. It stood in a huge brown pot in a recess at the end of the building. He looked at it quickly and saw with surprise that it was green and healthy. Its fan-like leaves were half closed, but he touched one with his hand and it closed still more.

He felt he must cry out with exultation. He took the pot into his arms. It was very heavy, so he got his knife and cut the plant out of the brown mould. He crept towards the exit with his treasure firmly clutched. He waited a few minutes and heard the sentry pass once more. Then he braced himself together and commenced to glide swiftly through the garden. He climbed the wall and made towards the wood. A quarter of a mile was covered safely, and then suddenly he heard a challenge in German not fifty yards from him. He stopped dead, then, gathering all his strength, rushed headlong. There was a loud report and a fearful pain in his breast. Still he proceeded, swaying from side to side in intense agony. A shell-hole would have brought him to earth, but miraculously he missed them. There were voices all around him, and a terrible red glare every-where. Then he saw a figure come from the bewildering gloom. Nearer and nearer it came, and he saw with surprise—his mother. " Why, mother," he gasped, " what are you doing here ? " But she only smiled and murmured something, and then suddenly he knew what she was saying, and he followed the words as her lips formed them :—

> For love, and beauty, and delight,
> There is no death nor change : their might
> Exceeds our organs, which endure
> No light, being themselves obscure.

Somebody was leaning over him holding a lantern before his face and the hum of voices sounded in his ears, but what they said he knew not, and it all seemed miles and miles away. Then he remembered his treasure and strove to lift it, but his muscles were no longer servant to his will, so with a great last effort he raised his head a few inches and gazed at that which lay within his arms, murmuring in a faint, fugitive voice :—

" The Sensitive Plant !—The Sensitive Plant ! "

GEO. GOODCHILD,
ROYAL GARRISON ARTILLERY,

THAT BLOKE BATES

By WHITING-BAKER

'E BLUNDERED down the blighted
    trench,
  The great big-footed clod,
Fell on me, an' knocked me down,
  Then on me pipe 'e trod ;
        Trod on, an' broke me bloomin' pipe,
          The only one I 'ad,
        Snapped it 'orf just near the bowl.
          Gawd ! I weren't arf mad.

An' 'e's the bloke as Saved the Guns,
  That blunderin' awkward blighter,
For since we "called upon" the 'Uns
  'E's been a nasty fighter.
But me, I'm invalided 'ome,
  For I copped a chunk of shell
Right upon me blinkin' 'ip.
  Oh, ain't it puffic 'ell !

An' as I limped along the street
  Outside the Pallis Gates,
Who'd ye think that I should meet
  But Mr. blushin' Bates !
'Is arm slung up ; yes, there he sat
  Be'ind some swanky 'osses,
Been to call upon the King
  For one of them there crosses.

The crowd they yelled thesselves all 'oarse,
  Which they some'ow cawn't be blamed.
"An 'oos the man as got ' The Crorss ' ? "
  Some nearby gent exclaimed.
"Gent," I says, "I knows the bloke,
  I does, so 'elp me swipe—
" ' 'E's Privit Bates, the swab who broke
  Me favrit' bloomin' pipe."

2ND-LIEUT. A. E. WHITING BAKER.
4TH BRITISH WEST INDIES REGT.

61

ADVICE TO YOUNG "SUBS"

A MISINTERPRETATION

The Message: Send Re-inforcements — we are about to advance —

Is passed down the line

& delivered:

Send three & fourpence — we are going to a dance.

!!!

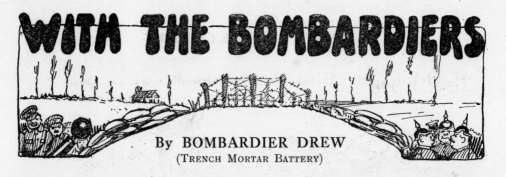

WITH THE BOMBARDIERS

By BOMBARDIER DREW
(Trench Mortar Battery)

THERE are two officers and twenty-four men in a 2″ Howitzer Battery. This statement does not reflect any discredit on the officers, because, properly speaking, everything below the rank of Supernumerary Unpaid Acting-Bombardier, who wears one stripe, is referred to officially as a man.

The instrument of murder which they affect consists of a little gun, which I dare not describe, but which fires a big round bomb weighing 50 lb. over an extreme range of — yards. This bomb is stuck at the end of a steel stick which fits into the barrel of the gun, and is forcibly ejected by means of cordite.

This stick has an unfortunate knack of returning to our own trenches when the bomb goes off, and I have designed an effective hook for use therewith for the purpose of bringing back stray prisoners, or perhaps some Delicatessen. So far, however, the conservative War Office authorities have not seen their way clear to adopt my suggestions.

An N.C.O. and two men work one of these guns, which are placed in various blind alleys, or bays along the ditch, dignified by the name of front-line trench. The mystic letters N.C.O. are not now so cabalistic as they once were; they mean "non-commissioned officer," i.e. an officer who is not commissioned. There are five N.C.O.'s in a trench mortar battery. They are referred to by serious papers like the *Times* and the *Bystander* as the backbone of the British Army. Of course, I refer to N.C.O.'s in general and not the particular specimens in our battery. N.C.O.'s in a trench-mortar battery are chiefly employed in pulling a piece of string, called by the learned a lanyard, which fires the gun, and in withdrawing safety-pins. These safety-pins are not of the variety known to ladies and conscientious objectors (pardon me, ladies, for coupling you), but are part of a device on the fuse of the bomb, which ensures safe handling and which would prevent the thing from going off at all if not withdrawn before firing, when a useful instrument of slaughter would be turned into a harmless "dud." "Dud" is a generic term for everything that ought to go off but doesn't. Such a tragedy of artillery sometimes occurs even when the safety-pin has not been left in, but when you watch the bomb sailing over gloriously at the end of its stick to the German lines, watch it fall gracefully, and then it does go off, and you look out with Machiavellian glee for bits of Germans and sausages in the huge funnel of stuff that erupts, it is simply great. That sentence is rather involved, but the U-boat-commander sort of feeling is the REAL THING.

Of course it must not be imagined that this is all. There are two sides to successful warfare : one is to kill Germans, the other is to prevent Germans from killing you. Disregard of the second would prove just as effective a method of finishing the war as enthusiastic attention to the first. There are many things to be dodged, and some of their trench-mortar bombs and grenades and things actually wobble in their course, which is rather disconcerting. Other things explode right by you without giving you any warning that they are coming. Others, on the other hand, come through the air like motor-buses changing gear, and seem to be all round you at once. There are other things, of course, such as snipers and maxims and things that are not worth mentioning.

Speaking seriously, however, it is the strain that is so wearing. The pretty continuous job and tear at the nerves will pull the best man to pieces. In the trenches a man is continually stretched on an intangible rack as real and as hideous as the instrument of the Inquisitor. The presence of danger is not so awful as its manifestations.

Let us suppose the daily strafe is over. It consists of an hour or so when the exchange of civilities between the lines is more violent than during the rest of the day.

A few men are blown to pieces, some more crippled, a

woman's heart is broken, a father's hopes are withered, and the report is issued that there is "nothing doing" on that particular sector.

Our N.C.O. and his fellow-murderers wade, covered with glory and mud, to their dugout, which is a cave in the ground, or, maybe, a shed in the trench, just high enough to allow one to walk about comfortably on one's knees. If you stand, your head is bent just enough to allow an uninterrupted passage to an icy drop of water, which will fall from the roof on to the nape of your neck and roll unobtrusively down your spine. The N.C.O. or man so attacked will immediately swear, straighten his back, bump his head, swear again, and subside in hopeless disgust on his blanket in the corner.

Probably at dawn, after a night spent chiefly in hunting beasts as voracious as the Huns themselves, and in arguing forcibly over the number of square inches of blanket that you consider your fair portion, you will be called upon to retaliate to the Germans' morning hate. You will rush out, with one boot half on, your trousers coming down, and if you have been having breakfast, with your face well "smarmed" with bread-crumbs and jam, to repeat the comedy.

THE NEO-TROGLODYTES

I DON'T remember much about the evening we got there. Thirty or forty *kilos* with full packs, extra rounds, smoke helmet, etc., and about six months' pay worth of *chocolat*, *petits pains*, and the like to provide against the rations going astray, and a few falls into shell-holes, during the last *kilo*, with a couple of hours' shuffling backwards and forwards in the trenches till we were sorted out into our proper sections, had made me disinclined to be critical. We simply wriggled in somehow, the five of us; wriggled out of our equipment, extracted, by violent contortions, cigarettes or chocolate from pockets and haversacks; and then wriggled into the least uncomfortable positions possible, and went to sleep. People who write for second-rate magazines always speak of a " deep and dreamless slumber" in these cases. Deep it may have been. Dreamless it wasn't. The flares we'd seen going up all the evening (awfully useful things, flares; if the Bosche only knew how useful they are for dodging shell-holes he'd chuck using 'em straight off), and the head-achey row of some of our guns had somehow reminded me of the war the papers say is going on, and I suppose I'd become bloodthirsty. Anyway, I was in the middle of a most splendiferous scrap, and I'd already spiked about six of the brutes, in spite of one who'd got round to the rear and was steadily boring into my back with his bayonet, when all of a sudden a huge Prussian Guardsman hurled himself on top of me. It's always in moments of stress that my true value shows itself. Seizing him dauntlessly round the middle with some Jiu-Jitsu hold I've forgotten the name of, I swung him round like a club, and, for all the growing wound in my back, should have simply annihilated the blighter in another minute, if those other silly blighters, Brown and Jones, hadn't squealed out like the miserable spoil-sports they were. Jones, at

67

any rate, might have had the decency to keep quiet, because it was his pack I was bashing 'em with. If he was going to hang it on a wobbly nail he might at least have hung it over his own head. And it was the sharp corner of Brown's mess-tin that had been wounding me in the back. Anyway, when we'd done telling as much as we could remember of our reciprocal opinions, we went to sleep again.

Then I had a horrible dream that I was back at Tidworth. It was dinner-time, and I was wrestling with a huge mouthful of roast meat. At least it must have been roast, because it was so tough, but it tasted like stew the day after the cook's night before, when they'd boiled the chemicals in the remains of the Epsom-salted tea from breakfast. I kept chewing it for an hour or so, but it never seemed to get any softer. The taste only got worse. Then, just as I was getting my teeth into it, some rude bounder snatched it out of my very mouth, and through a sort of haze came Jones' silly voice asking what the blood-stained Pluvonian realms I thought I was biting his toe for? I do hate the sort of man who spills his *vin rouge* down your neck, and then curses you because it's wasted. "If you can't keep your boots out of my mouth, Private Jones," I observed cuttingly, "you—— (words failed me), well, you know where you can shove 'em!"

Anyway, even after that we got to sleep again, and it was only the call of "Stand down" that waked us. If only we'd heard it more distinctly it would have been all right, because we'd simply have lain low, but unfortunately we thought it was "Stand to," and promptly proceeded to turn out, or at least to get ready to turn out. If we'd kept quiet they'd probably have thought our dugout was unoccupied. As it was, the spectacle of Robinson squirming out through the doorway with his equipment round his legs, and his rifle behind his ear, and the rest of us pushing behind him, quite gave the show away.

It's disgusting how greedy people all seem to be about rations. There were five of *us*, and only four others, including the Corporal, in the Section. When I went along to get our share of the Section's bacon, I cut a piece off, only ever so little more than our proper share, but the row the Corporal kicked up was simply abominable. It wasn't my fault. Both ends were fat, and the middle was lean, and I *had* to include the middle with our end. Of course I stuck to what I'd got, and snaffled all the butter and jam, too, just to teach him not to be so beastly greedy. There was an awful hunt for that, later, in which I helped most unselfishly. I finally brought it home to the Platoon Sergeant. What he and the Corporal said to each other was a joy for ever.

Unfortunately, during "Stand to" the other dugouts had pinched all the braziers. We borrowed one dugout's brazier while they were looking for wood, and another's wood while they were fighting for rations. That meant that we had to have the fire inside till the subsequent shindy had subsided.

Of course some silly ass of an N.C.O. *would* shout out that we were all to draw shovels and start fatigue just as the bacon was half fried. Fortunately we heard him shouting some way off long before he came near us, so we all scurried into the dugout, put the brazier in the doorway, and blew out the candle. When he came to the door there was a fight for the farthest and darkest corner. "Come on out," he called. "I know who's in there." "Liar," we breathed silently. He was rather a wily N.C.O., and went away. A few minutes later he returned. We hadn't been such fools as to emerge or light the candle. "Volunteers to go back to Blightie," he requested. The suggestion was too much. "Lor'!" we murmured in yearning and ecstatic concert. "Brown and Williams!" came the triumphant rejoinder. "I know your voices. Double out, all of you!" Jones and Mac and I lay low, and congratulated ourselves. Just like that blighter Brown to tread on my face as he got out. Naturally I yelled. That left only Jones and Mac. When you come to think of it, it is a rotten trick to slack about and let other people do your work for you. I began to get quite annoyed with Jones and Mac. By the time I'd crawled through them, put my hand on an open jam tin, and barked my shins on the brazier, my indignation simply couldn't be stifled. "Come on, Jones, you slacker!" I shouted. "Come on, Mac. It's a dirty trick to be skulking about in here like this when there's work that's got to be done." The profanity amid which the pair slowly and reluctantly emerged was positively appalling. Some people have *no* conscience.

Well, of course the next thing was to slip off from the fatigue and get back to our breakfasts. By the time we'd fried the bacon and boiled, one at a time, four billies of water to make tea, and then warmed up the bacon and the first two billies, and eaten it all, and washed up and smoked an after-brekker cigarette, it really didn't seem worth while to start work before dinner.

Dinner is an awkward meal. Awkward to forage for, I mean. However, between what we'd been served out with, what we had of our own, what the previous occupants of the dugout had left behind, and what we found here, there, and everywhere, we had at our disposal more bullies and maconachies than we could possibly eat in a week; biscuits and cheese ditto, about a dozen potatoes, plenty of Oxo cubes, two packets of peasoup powder, a handful of onions—worth their weight in gold in the trenches, and, pride of our hearts, a turnip!

Men came hundreds of yards along the line to see that turnip, and gathered round it in envious and admiring crowds. The fame of it spread up to the fire trenches (it was the supports we were in), and probably even to the Bosche lines. Anyway, half a dozen shells came buzzing over and landed a hundred yards or so in a direct line behind our dugout.

In the afternoon, happy, satisfied, and replete, we dozed. The pig in the dugout, the sonorousness of our snores, the general atmosphere of peace, tranquillity, and drowsiness—all made up as fine a picture of an English home on a Sunday afternoon as Dickens himself could wish, though the harmony of the latter part was somewhat marred by everybody exhorting every one else to get up and get tea ready.

After tea tragedy overtook us. We all clicked for Ration Fatigue. It wasn't only the work we minded—it was the injury to our pride. Five of the finest and most expert dodgers in the Company and not one had escaped it! It transpired later that the whole Company was on it: we had to draw for the Companies in the firing line as well as for ourselves. The journey to the village a mile behind was all serene, but the journey back along a mile of shell-holed lane, with constant halts on account of flares and two sandbags of bully beef tins on one's back, and finally the slippery plank dance for a mile along the trenches, across ponds, under telephone wires, through six-inch-wide trenches where the sandbags had bulged in, was— Dantesque. *We* merely became incoherently profane.

Being conscientiously opposed to giving free puffs, I will not divulge the precise brand of beef-tea that cheered our souls, but a cup of —— steamin' 'ot, *is* a real refresher.

Then to bed (why will that phrase stick?)—to dream of a steaming hot bath, with piles of clean, dry towels, and a good stiff peg of—milk—and lemon, and a bed—a real live (not in the entomological sense) bed with real sheets and pillows and things . . . Ah-h-h!

A day in the trenches!—and to think of my affectionate family fondly and fearfully picturing me in a hurricane of Jack Johnsons, bareheaded and barefooted, in heroic headlong charge, bayoneting the Bosche! Yet such is war.

TWOPENCE.

"Squaddies."

ENCYCLOPÆDIA OF MILITARY TERMS

(Continued)

ENGINEERS.—The wise men of the army. They teach the ignorant infantry how to carry sandbags, barbed wire, bath mats, etc., and how to work intricate machinery such as picks and shovels.

ESTAMINET.—Translated into English means the "Rendez-vous de la Police Militaire." It is where soldiers (including engineers) congregate to spend their unearned increment and to recount the many brave deeds they have done, also to listen to Mademoiselle's "Arf an' Arf" language whilst drinking her "Arf an' Arf" beer.

FORM FOURS.—All military experts agree that it is absolutely imperative that a man be able to form fours before he is fit to defend the Empire.

Although this intricate manœuvre can be accomplished in any number of movements a Drill Instructor usually recommends three. The odd number stands pat, the even numbers step on somebody's toes in the rear with the left foot, and somebody's heel on the right with the right foot. The even number will then find himself viewing the landscape on the back of the odd number's neck, whilst the Empire totters.

Lack of space prevents forming fours in the trenches, but the War Office has the matter under consideration.

(From *The Listening Post.*)

"With the Army.'   (1) Teaching recruits to " carry the left foot about 12 inches to the left."—*Vide* "Infantry Training, 1914."

73

⚜ IN THE TRENCHES ⚜

WE were certainly under the impression when we started that we were to end our journey in a trench. As it happened, it turned out to be a canal. Now, it must be obvious to anybody that a canal, being a precious thing in the sight of Cousin Fritz, it behoved us to make all possible provision for its defence. After all, you never know what the enemy has in his mind. Once let him get possession of that canal, and he might rebuild the German Navy there bit by bit, as it falls to pieces in its present lair. Of course this canal of ours had been a trench at one time. There was plenty of evidence as to this. The most convincing testimony on that point was undoubtedly Thompson's. He had been to the bottom to search for a sack of bully beef, which he had dropped over the edge, and when he returned it was with the intimation that he had found some trench boards down below. So, obviously this canal of ours had been a trench.

Well now, in view of possible attacks on the part of Fritz, we decided to make the canal almost as inaccessible to him as it had been to us. This was by no means an easy proposition.

Jimmie, who went out to reconnoitre round about the wire entanglements directly we arrived, came back with the report that the ground between seemed fairly flat as far as he could make out. Jimmie has the makings of a scout. How on earth he discovered, in the blackness of night, that that intervening hundred yards between ourselves and Fritz were flat (as it turned out in daylight they were), I shall never discover. He may have guessed it : if so, it was either a very clever or else a very lucky guess.

C'est magnifique!—mais ce n'est pas la guerre.— (From *The Gasper*.)

No, it was obvious to us that try how we might during that forty-eight hours to make it otherwise, Fritz' approach to our trench would nevertheless be more straightforward than our own. For consider the many adventures that befell us that night as we made our way thither with a strong nor'-easter blowing across our path. It is impossible to avoid the use of nautical language in considering that voyage. The very thought of it brings all sorts of sailor-like language to our lips. It certainly gives one a certain sense of satisfaction to be able to hear the mud go " squelch, squelch " beneath a pair of waders, but when it comes to a question of balancing oneself in them on a six-inch plank with a sack of bully on one arm and a number of loaves in the other, the advantages of the knee boot are lost in the difficulty one experiences in preserving one's equilibrium in spite of the almost unrestrainable desire of the boots to go forward at any cost and prove their worth by plunging headlong into the flood beneath. With a certain amount of luck, however, you might be trusted to arrive at the canal, your ultimate destination, with possibly one loaf and at least a dozen tins of bully, the remainder of your cargo having previously fallen overboard during perhaps several moments of suspense—literally and other- wise—when you had found yourself dangling by your legs from a perverse beam, vainly endeavouring to keep your head out of the water.

Well, to come to our plans for the defence of our canal. We decided at the outset that the parapet must be heightened. After all, six feet four of humanity requires a fair pile of sand- bags in front of it before it can settle the question of how to satisfy fifteen men with one loaf of bread and forty-eight tins of bully. In point of fact, there was nothing wherewith the process could be carried out, nor any prospect of finding anything, until Jimmie announced that he had encountered a sandbag at the bottom of the canal, while he was floundering about there in search of his rations. Jimmie earned the D.C.M. three times over by volunteering to recover it, and it was at once filled with mud. It is a peculiarity of these sandbags that though they are bags they are never filled with sand. This may be because as there is nothing else around but mud, the use of sand is out of the question. At all events, there aren't really any sandbags in France except in the stories of the special correspondents.

Having thus heightened our parapet to the extent of one mudbag, there remained nothing more to be done but to settle down and await events.

It might have been a very dull evening had not Fritz provided us with a band, which discoursed melodies for an hour or so, and awoke memories of the seaside in England a couple of years ago. Possibly it will be objected that a German band is not a very satisfactory source of excitement. But Fritz knows that his band is not sufficient entertainment for us ; so he lets us have a display of fireworks every quarter of an hour or so. A German starshell is not only as picturesque as a Crystal Palace rocket ; it has besides a certain amount of utility. You may utilize a starshell in many ways. They are, for instance, distinctly useful as a help in spreading Army bread with Army jam, by means of an Army knife : they are not to be sneezed at as tolerably efficient substitutes for radium in one's watch.

So we thanked Fritz silently for these favours and continued to wait. Life in the trenches, after all, is just one long wait and sea (no pun intended). At present we wait. One day we shall see.

Bow-Wow.

(From *The Gasper*.)

Blimy !

An Anzac Convalescent. *Study by L.-Cpl. Geo. J. Coates.*

ANZAC SLANG

A CONVERSATION I caught the other day might prove mystifying to the uninitiated.

"Hullo, chum! I've just heard some bonza news."

"What! Another furfie?" "No, dinkum oil this time; the boys have imshied the Turks on the right, and got fifty prisoners, who say they have had mafeesh tucker for two days."

Half of it is Egyptian Arabic, picked up in Cairo, like the Gippy children's reiterated "Give it baksheesh," which the men are very fond of using.

Bonza corresponds with our "ripping" or "top-hole."

A furfie is a rumour, and dinkum means "genuine," and dinkum oil means "authenticated news." Imshi is Gippy for "clear out" or "get away," and mafeesh, which is borrowed from the same tongue, means "nothing." Tucker, of course, has the same meaning as our "grub."

When an Australian wishes to acquire something he "shakes it," whereas the British Tommy either "makes it" or "scrounges it," in the same way as on a larger scale Governments "annex" things. Tommy's slang is largely derived from Hindustani, and includes such words as "chipperow" for "shut up," "put some jildi into it," meaning "hurry up," and "let's have a dekko," when he wants to have a look at something.

"Pozzy" is jam—"cherb," beer—"rooty," bread—"dough," money — "jippo," gravy — "muckim," butter — "char," tea. "Swinging the lead" is pretending or deceiving, while "chucking his weight about" is self-explanatory, and denotes an aggressive or bullying manner. When an article is "spare" it means that it is not wanted, or, more usually, if a man says he "found it lying about spare," it is a euphemistic way of saying that the owner did not happen to be looking after it at the moment.

"TRANSPORT OFFICER" IN GALLIPOLI.

(From *The 3rd London General Hospital Gazette*.)

GALLIPOLI

H. K. ELCOCK.

"This is only B4 trying to steal our gramophone."

(*By a patient in B3.*)

(From *The 3rd London General Hospital Gazette*.)

LEAVES FROM A
SOLDIER'S DIARY

*The following is an exact copy of a portion of a diary found by Captain Nowell J. Sievers in the German fire trench before the quarries at Hulluch. It dates from October 19, 1914, to March 8, 1915, and was presumably written by an N.C.O. of the first Expeditionary Force. I have refrained from correcting the errors in grammar and punctuation since in its rough original state it has a vividness which would almost certainly be lost by editorial treatment.—*EDITOR.

. . . close by and commence diging a trench 5 feet deep while we were diging the Germans Artillary started shelling 2nd Gordon and Royal Engineers on our left flank who were entrenching themself. Our Artillary at once replied with a verry hot shell fire and soon quietened them for the night.

October 20th.

At 9 a.m. the next morning we moved from our position and advanced in Artillary formation to a open field by were the 2nd Gordons had entrenched themself the previos day and there we remain for 2 hrs during which time we were getting milk and apples from a farm close by us. Every think was going splendidly to we were about to have dinner when all of a sudden the Germans Artillary open a murderous shrapnel fire upon us our Regement was verry lucky in only having two men wounded.

October 21st.

Orders came down the line about 2 kilometers and there in trench ourself for a big battle while we doing so the Germans Artillary open fire with there guns and gave us a hot time. the 2nd Gordens and Scotch Guards went out and drew the fire while we were diging the trenches for them and ourself. The Scotch Guards lost 2 men 2nd Gordons 5 and the Borders 15 killed and wounded.

F

Maae in the Trenches

October 22nd.

On the 22nd about 9 a.m. the sad news came down the line that Capt. Clancey and Sgt. Spikely were killed and Pte. Hunt had lost one eye, which was all caused by the explosion of a Jack Johnson on the roof of a farm close to the trench were they had apparantly been having Breakfast. About 9.45 a.m. NO 16 Pontoon under the orders Lut. Johnston reinforced Lut. Gerrard Pontoon under hot shell and maxim fire.

. . . down by there snipers we got orders to fall in and return to Head Quarters and when we mustered up we found out that we had lost all told 723 men killed and wounded and 8 Officers. So we rested at Head Quarters for the night and on the 28th we marched to a wood close by at 9 a.m. Orders came along that we were to advance in skirmishing order over an open field close by. When we had gone 2 kilometers the Officer commanding the Regt. (Colonel L. I. Woods) got shot in the leg and as we were passing him he said " Go straight on the men of the Borders do not wait for me." And then the command fell to Lut. watson. The position we were attacking was too strong for us so we had to retire back to the trenches that had been left by the Gordons. In the advance we lost 82 men killed and wounded. We remained in the trenches till dusk and then returned back to our dugout and rested for the night.

November 21st.

Relived from the trenches by the 2nd Gordons.

November 22nd.

Had a draft sent out to us they arrived on the 21st November they were inspected by the General in charge of the 7th Div.

November 24th.

Returned back to trenches found it took us $4\frac{1}{2}$ hours to go 2 miles owing to the German Snipers at work at the communication trench leading to the firing line 2 men killed and 4 wounded fighting all night 7 men wounded.

November 25th.

Snipers at work shot 6 men getting water killing 2 and wounded 4. 9.15 one man shot in the eye which blinded him was taken to hospital and died same night.

Leaves from a Soldier's Diary

November 25th.

Told of to go and draw rations with 11 men. We got rations safe but coming back 5 men got shot 3 killed and 2 wounded so we lost half of the rations so A. and C Company had to go on half rations the next day.

November 26th.

Relived out of trenches raining in torrance wet through and up to the knees mud 2 men of the Borders killed one officer of the Royal Engineers killed and 2 men of the Scots Guards wounded.

November 27th.

Had a bath rather a luxury still raining. Never saw the sun for a week.

November 28th.

Little better weather more reinforcements at night went out diging trenches 400 yards from German Trenches started raining and never left off got wet through under fire all the time 2 men killed and 3 wounded. And it took 7 hrs to do 1 hrs work.

November 29th.

Returned to trenches heavy firing all the time. Fighting all night.

November 30th.

One man looking over trench got shot in the Head died same day.

December 1st.

Lieut Cotch killed while looking over through lop hole one of the best Officers in the Border Regt. and he was lied to rest at 12 m.n same day.

December 2nd.

Relived out of trenches and went for 8 days to Merville for rest.

December 10th.

Returned to Sailly and had a bath.

December 11th.

Went into trenches and I think it was the best fight we had all the time we were in the trenches as it was a fight for 3 days and I can tell you it was good go as we were well entrenched and could have a good go at them as far as I could find out only 12 men killed and 4 wounded but the Germans must had lost heavy as they seem to leave off all at once.

December 12th.

Relived out of trenches march back to our Billets.

December 15th.

Went and had a bath and a clean change of washing.

December 16th.

Received my first pay 20 Franks which amounted to 16/8 and it caused a great commotion when they shouted turn out for pay.

December 17th.

Received orders to stand too as we were going down to the trenches to make a charge. We go to the trenches but the charge was cancelled as the night was too light to make a charge. Remained in the trenches all night.

December 18th.

It was about 4.45 p.m. when the Officer came down the trench and told us there was going to be a charge that night. And it was to take place at 6 p.m. And then you could hear the men praying to God to look after there wife and children should anythink happen to them, the orders came down the line that we were to get through our own barbed wire and then wait for the signal to make the Charge which was to be the blast of a whistle which was to be blown by Capt. Askew. We waited till 6 p.m. but never heard the signal so A and C Comp. made the Companys for the charge with B and D Companys as our supports the Scotch Guards on our right and the 2nd Gordons on our left. Somehow or the other our left was to soon with the charge and as soon as there voices went up so did the German lead and they let us have it. We followed them but we were going down like raindrops as our trenches was only 70 yds apart so we retired and then made the second charge but received the same. We retired again and stoped in mid field and it was like being in a Blacksmith shop watching him swing a hammer on a red hot shoe and the sparks flying all round you but instead of them being sparks they were bullets. As the Germans had a inferlated fire on us and we lieyed there it was a pitiful sight to see and hear our comrades dyeing and could not get to help them as it ment serten death if we moved. Then Orders came down the line for us to retire to the trenches. But we could not do so as the fire was too heavy. After laying out there for 6½ hrs most of us manage to get back while others got shot about 5 yards from our own trenches in trying to get back. Ther was 18 men with me. We were so close that we dare not move if we would not have live to tell the tale. So we had to lay there from 6.20 to 8.15 a.m. the next morning. And as a Angle sent down from Heaven it came over verry misty and this being our only chance we made good of it. So we crawl half way and then made a run for it. We could not see were we were going so fell over our comrades who were dead, as we were making our trenches as we were about to drop in the trench we were challenged with our own men for the Regt. name Platoon we belong to so we got into our trench at 8.15 that morning after the charge. And I must say I think it the first time I said my prayers in earnest which is nothing to my credit for when I looked round and saw my chums I thanked God he had spared me there fate. At 10 a.m. we were taken to the Reserve Trench and had a roll call. And then we found out that Capt. Askew and Capt. Lane were wounded Capt. Lane being taken to Hospital. But we treid to find Capt. Askew but he could not be found. And as we being marched back to the Billets as we were passing Brigadier General he said to a Capt. on his staff "I am sorry for the 2nd Border they have had a verry hard hit in this Campaign." We reached our Billets at 5 p.m. and there we had another Roll Call.

A. Company lost 85⎫ 148
B. Company lost 63⎭

We were having supper when news came down to our Billets that a lot of our Company were laying on the field wounded and had to be got in at all cost A. and B.

December 20th.

About 10.35 a.m. when the doctor saw 2 men out on the German barb wire and said them too men are alive so get them in so 2 men went out that night and get them in and when they get into our trenches they said give me a smoke and a drink of water. Now these two men been out for 52 hrs and how they live no one knows but thank God they are all right now and doing well.

December 21st.

This being my Birthday I spent resting in the Trench with a good dinner of corned Beef and had a sing song with my chums.

December 25th. Xmas Day.

On Xmas morning about 5.30 a.m. a German officer showed a white flag on the trench and about 10 mts after came on the top himself and walked half way across to our trench and asked to see one of our Officers of the English Army, so a Officer of the Scots Guards went out to meet him they talked for a time and then returned to there trenches, and no sooner had the German Officer returned when there voices shouted out a happy Xmas to all you English so we wished them the same. At the time we were fighting against the Bavarians. About 8 a.m. we saw them get out of there trench and asked us not to fire as they wanted to keep the Peace that day as it was Xmas day so we did not fire that day. At 9 a.m. they came half way and we went to meet them. And the first thing they asked us when are you going to give in you are beat. So we asked them who told them all this and they pointed to a paper they had in there hand and they told us pointblank that they had troops reviewing in Hyde Park and also troops in Calais. Well me and my chum couldn't help laughing at them and they looked at us and couldn't make it out. So I said to them well I must admit that you have got troops in London but they are Prisoners of War. They would not take that so my chum gave them the News of the World and they thanked us and gave us a segar to smoke. At 11.15 Orders came along that we were to fall in as the Officer wished to speak to us so we all returned and found that we were to bury our Comrades that fell in the Charge on the 18th of Dec. so we all started diging and burying them side by side and made a Cross out of the wood of a Biscuit box and layed them to rest on Xmas Day when we had finished we all kneled and offered up a Pray to God above for our Comrades who fell in Honour. We were having tea when the Germans started singing God save the King in as good English as they could. And then three cheers went up from our trenches. So we all had a good sing song that night in our trenches. But we did not forget to have our look out as I do not think we became friends. And it was hear that we heard of the fate of Capt. Askew a German Officer gave one of our Officers the Cap and collar badges of our late Officer and told him that they had buried him behind there firing line and put these words on his grave.

Here lies a brave British Officer
Captain Askew.

December 26th.

Nothing doing in particular.

December 31st.

On guard waiting for 1915 to come in and my old chum Jack Rae singing the Old Year out and the New Year in and think of home and them we love wishing all them a happy New Year.

January 1st.

Dismounted Guard at 12 a.m. after doing 24 hrs Guard was ordered for the trench at 4.45 p.m. reached there at 5.45 p.m.

January 3rd.

Diging all day in water up to our knees and raining all the time. I do not think I have put in a worst day since out here I have been.

January 4th.

At 10.15 the General and Staff inspected our trenches and come and look at our dugout and said it was the best one along the line. And also spoke of the cover we had made for the Explosive Bombs which was our work in the Firing Line.

Made in the Trenches

January 5th.

At 10 a.m. the British Artillary started shelling German Trenches and doing good work.

January 6th.

British Artillary going at it, Jack Johnson coming over frequently. Heavy fighting in the trenches at 3.30 p.m.

January 7th.

Heavy fighting on left flank. I received orders to take 6 men to get wood from R.E. Head Quarters 1 mile from firing line. While going had the most luckest escape of my life to shots at me one going right through my valise and I think that was the quickest move of my life in taking cover. I had 2 men wounded out of the 8 and returned back wet through.

January 8th.

Spent a quiet day nothing doing verry bad weather raining in torrance relived out of trenches at 8.35 p.m.

January 9th.

Mounted Guard 12 midnight. At 8.15 had a German spy brought in dress as a woman could speak English verry well.

January 10th.

Went and had a bath.

January 11th.

Received orders to take 6 men down to the trenches the Germans when about 15 yards from our own trenches sent up a Wreck Light but before it gave the light we were on the ground but they must have seen us because they sent volley after volleys. But luck was with us as now one got hurt we had to stop there all 15 mts and then take to the trenches one after the other at 5 mts.

January 11th.

German and English Artillary going at it for $3\frac{1}{2}$ hrs.

January 12th.

Trenches flooded with water had to keep pumping for 12 hrs.

Leaves from a Soldier's Diary

January 13th.

Nothing doing in Reserve trenches.

January 14th.

Germans shelling our trenches which came to no good we started fighting at 10.45 a.m. and kept them bussy for 7 hrs. lost 25 killed and wounded.

January 15th.

At 4.45 Sgt. Hull got shot when he was going from one trench to another. He could not get to it without going over the top of his trench that when he—— he passed away 5 mts after.

January 16th.

We were all at ease when a Jack Johnson came over and knocked our trench in so we went to No. 9 and there took cover for 6 hrs and then returned to our trench and rebuilt it.

January 17th.

A German came and gave himself up and told us there was going to be an attack upon us at 12 midnight stood to all night nothing came of it.

January 18th.

Should have been relived at 6.45 but owing to some mistake our reliving party went astray did not get relived till 1.33 and then Orders came along the line that there was a guide to take us to a new post which was the Gordons trench. But owing to it being a black night the guide lost his way so we were walking about $2\frac{1}{2}$ hrs. So in our walk we came to a German outpost he gave us 5 rounds rapid which was soon taken up by the German firing line and how 5 of us returned I do not know ther were 8 men and myself and with us we carried enough gun cotton and powder to blow up a castle. They kept up the fire about $\frac{1}{2}$ hr so we started crawling the way we came as we thought, but we went another way altogether all at wonce we heard a call for help and then found out that one of our men had fell into a stream. We got him out safe but the Germans had heard his shout for help and the bullets came over in dozens and I can see us all waiting to see who would be the next to go down. But luck happened 5 of us returned back out of the 8 then they sent up a wreck light and that show us the way to make for. So we made short dashes for our trenches which was the Gordons but about 15 yards away from our trench we were halted and I could not get the voice as the wind was blowing the other way so we lay down and then heard the Challenge again I gave the answer and when I got up to the trench I was told I was a lucky man as the hole of the trench was taking sight at my men and myself. I was taken to the Trench and saw the Officer and told him all that had happened. So he sent word not to fire as I was going out to fetch in wounded men and they were taken to Hospital that same night. The same night one of our wire cutters when out got shot in the leg.

February 16th.

Took 2 men to draw rations to dressing station about 1¾ from firing line we got just out of the trench and had gone 15 yards when we were fired on. We all fell to the ground in mud 6 in. deep, we went along as far as we could crawling along in the mud, we then made a fresh start we got about 300 yds from the firing line when 2 maxims were put on us till we fell again. I fell in a Jack Johnson hole and my too chums fell in a ditch up to there wastes and we had to wait in that position for half an hour. We made the third try we managed to get our rations. But we had to take the mud off of our close before we could make another start back. We reached back to the trench about 11.45 p.m. wet through and remain in the same close all night and next day.

February 16th.

One man shot in the head by a German sniper. About 3 p.m. Commander Samson in his Airplane was flying over the German lines taking observation of there position he was flying about for about ¾ of hr. and in that time he had 35 shrapnell shell and Rifle fire at him with no result. It was a good sight to see him leading the Germans a dance. About 3.45 word was sent along the line that Pte. Healy was killed by Bullets which must had been done by the Maxim Gun for when he was picked up he was riddled with Bullets. This man was looking at a Comrade grave which he had beryed on the 25th Dec. who met his death in the charge on the 18th December.

Leaves from a Soldier's Diary

February 17th.

Heavy firing on the Right continuously for 8 p.m. till dawn with slight intervals between excepting attack on our position according to information of captured Prisoners by the French on our Right they made an attack on our right wing but left our position alone. Relived out of trenches by 2nd Gordons. It was black night we could not make our way to Head Quarters. Got lost in communication trenches water up to our neck walked 4½ miles back to Billets wet through.

March 1st.

Returned to trenches.

March 2nd.

About 10.30 a.m. one of our aircraft was siking information of our enemy and the German guns open fire upon him in lest than 11 minutes he had 52 shrapnell at him but got away safely. At 5.15 p.m. english and German guns open at it for 2½ hrs. British silents these after putting them out of action. On this day 2 chums and myself had a chicken for tea which cost but little but it was good.

March 3rd.

We were relived by the 8th Res. at 10.15. On our return to Head Quarters we were about to get into the Communication trench when the Germans sent up a wreck light they open fire on us killing 2 men and wounded 3 of the 9 men on left owing to the night-hork which we fell against that gave us away by squeaking.

March 4th.

Fell in at 4.45. Left Sailly marched to Dupond reached there at 10.15. Road was verry bad for marching.

March 7th.

Left Dupond at 2 p.m. marched to V. Berguin reached there at 6.15.

March 8th.

Left for Ver Berguin at 11.15 a.m.

THE MISSING BANANA SKIN

"This spirit of economy reigns through every department of the hospital."

HAROLD BEGBIE in *The Daily Chronicle.*

1. The Loss is discovered.

2. All leave is immediately suspended.

3. The guard is doubled, and a lookout stationed on the water tower.

4. Suspicion falls on the Nite-awdlies.

THE MISSING BANANA SKIN (*continued*)

5. An officer is detailed by the C.O. to inquire into the matter.

6. The C.O. prepares a report
(Army form
$\dfrac{\text{T.04}}{\text{AC ppp}}$ (N.B.G.) 4·000 $\left[\dfrac{\text{A}}{\times \text{IB}}\right]$ $\frac{1}{4}$0.)
to the War Office.

7. The situation is saved by Sergt. Derwent Wood and Pte. Wilcoxson, who prepare a colourable imitation of the missing article, which being conveyed under cover of darkness within the precincts of the hospital—

8. Is providentially discovered by the Mainorlawdly in time to avert a national scandal.

PTE. STEPHEN B. DE LA BERE.

BALM IN GILEAD

I OFTEN pause and ponder
    In philosophic vein ;
My thoughts take wing and wander
    Till sergeants grow profane.
I think of times departed,
Before the shindy started,
When I was lighter-hearted,
    And all was right as rain.

I think how Piccadilly
    Beheld me cut a dash
With something fair and frilly,
    Or mopping Scotch and Splash—
How throats were wide and porous,
How sweetly smiled the chorus—
And how it used to bore us
    And swallow all the cash.

A Crœsus' glinting mintage,
    A Venus' witching wiles,
A Nectarean vintage
    Could scarcely tempt our smiles—
All *blasé*, bored, and *ennui'd*,
And discontented when we'd
All that we now think men need
    And which the need of riles !

Balm in Gilead

A barn all bare and draughty,
    Where, though the largest leaks
Are plugged by fingers crafty,
    Between the tiles are streaks
Of sky all clouds and rainfall,
Where hopes of ease in vain fall,
And showers of words profane fall
    And many kinds of reeks—

A wisp of mouldy, musty,
    And populated straw,
Whose inhabitants are lusty
    And quick with fang and claw—
Yet drowsier and lazier
As smoke of pipe and brazier
Grows heavier and hazier,
    I to such pallet draw

With high ecstatic rapture
    For dreams of Blighty-bliss
That pillows ne'er could capture
    And eiderdowns would miss—
To dream of days pre-bellic,
Or posts, when I, worn relic,
Return to the angelic . . .
    And then to wake to—*this!*

And evenings still are cheery
    In cosy village pubs
For swain or swaddy weary
    Who smokes or swigs or grubs.
Estaminet or taproom—
It matters not a rap—room
To sit, while in the chap room
    Awaits the mellow mugs!

95

Made in the Trenches

To grousers be it granted !—
  Canonic British Beer
Is doctored or supplanted
  And foams not for us here ;
But *Vin* (the *Rouge* or *Blanc* kind—
For me they're both the wrong kind—
We may not buy the strong kind)
  Brings strictly sober cheer.

O spectacle pathetic !—
  Myself who love Old Ale,
Sipping some Strange Emetic
  Or Bass gone flat and stale !
I take (O deep devotion !)
Vin Blanc, and with emotion
Pretend the putrid potion
  Is Scotch because it's pale.

O frugal now and meagre
  The balm my soul doth seek—
To be a non-fatiguer,
  A wash say once a week,
Cargo for little Mary—
To ask of Fate the chary
Aught more would be contrary,
  Cussèd, confounded cheek !

TWOPENCE.

(From *The Gasper*.)

"And the WOODBINE spices are wafted abroad."

TENNYSON.

TOMMY ATKINS, LINGUIST

It is surprising the number of words which our soldiers have adopted for their own use, both from the language of their Allies and foes. Tommy is very fond of the word " strafe," and is nearly as frequent in its use as are the Germans themselves. Strange to relate, Tommy has always shown himself to be strongly in favour of Hindustani, with the knowledge of which language he has considerably increased his vocabulary. Hindustani appears to have always been the most favoured language, for even in the days of the Boer War, the words " posee," " rooty," and " pawnee," meaning, jam, bread, and water, respectively, were freely used and understood by all our soldiers. Blighty (or Blightie) is a word the origin of which has been responsible for much discussion. When I first heard the word " blighty " used in France I had not the slightest knowledge of its meaning. I knew that the word was a stranger to Yorkshire and its dialect ; neither had it found its origin in Lancashire (I know Lancashire well—I once passed through in a train !), but I was afterwards informed by one who can speak with authority on this question that the word " blighty " is one of the many words adopted from the language of Tommy's Indian Ally. The Mohammedan word " wilayat " or " bilayat " originally meant " own district." To the Sepoy in India, this " bilayat " stands for England, the district in his comprehension of his officers, who, of course, are English. Everything English is "bilaiti," and every British officer speaks to the natives of England as "wilayat" or "bilayat." When Tommy adopted the word he added the "y," hence "blighty."

The expression "cushy one" is also adopted from the same language. "Cushy one" comes from the Indian "Khush," meaning happiness, and "khushi" meaning happy. When Tommy refers to his wound as a "cushy one," it is the wound which, in his opinion, will assure him a trip to England, or "Blighty." The following lines, which I believe were written by a private in the Worcestershire Regiment, very aptly express Tommy's affection for "Blighty," after a long spell of Hun-hunting.

I've travelled many journeys in my one score years and ten,
And oft enjoyed the company of jovial fellow-men;
But of all the happy journeys, none can compare to me
When the Red Cross special night express from the trenches to the sea.

Chorus.
It's Balloo,[1] Boulogne, and Blighty
Is the burden of my song,
Balloo, Boulogne, and Blighty,
Oh! speed the train along.
If you've only half a stomach,
And you haven't got a knee,
You'll choke your groans and try to shout the chorus out with me—
Balloo, Boulogne, and Blighty,
Dear old Blighty 'cross the sea.

Now some of us are mighty bad, and some are wounded slight,
And some will see their threescore years; but some won't last the night;
But the Red Cross train takes up the strain, all in a minor key,
And sings "Boulogne and Blighty" as she rumbles to the sea.

Chorus. "It's Balloo, etc."

Oh! it's better than the trenches, and it's better than the rain,
It's better than the mud and stink; and we're going home again.
We're going home to Blighty just as jolly as can be,
Though most of us leave some of us the wrong side of the sea.

Chorus. "It's Balloo, etc."

[1] "Balloo" is Tommy's corruption of Bailleul.

Tommy Atkins, Linguist

We're a train of blooming cripples; but we ain't down-hearted—no!
There's a holy peace about this train, for we guess that we shall go
Across the shiny Channel that lies 'twixt her and me,
To the one and only Blighty, our Blighty 'cross the sea,
Where the blooming Hun can never come—our home across the sea.

Chorus. "It's Balloo, etc."

British soldiers who have fraternized with Indian troops speak of "C.B." (confined to barracks) as "off the chowki," which is taken from the Indian word "chauki," which has exactly the same meaning. Words have come over from India with the troops long before the Emperor of Germany commenced to issue ultimatums. "I don't care a dam!" for instance, has the dam correctly spelt without an "n," for it is taken from the Indian "dam"—the smallest copper coin.

I have heard the expression "I don't care a dam!" used by meek curates as well as County Councillors, and very amateur golfers. A plus man does not necessarily make use of the same dam. He is a poor army adjutant who has to resort to the use of this expression, yet a regular church-goer considers it bordering on the wicked, and paving the way to (saved by Censor) to murmur "I don't care tuppence"—which is more than a dam!

Of course, to "care a dam" and to "dam a thing" are two entirely different things. The latter involves certain operations, whereas the former does not.

For my own use I prefer "Tut-tut."

Lots of soldiers use this expression. Lots don't!

HERBERT E. GOFTEN.

(From *The Yorkshire Post*.)

"On the right form—Squad!——!!!!!"—D. COWLE.

99

YEOMEN'S LIFE IN EGYPT

THE COOKHOUSE

HORSE-FLY TROUBLE

'IF MY MOTHER COULD SEE ME NOW!'

LED HORSES UP

100

"TALLY HO!"
AN INCIDENT
ON MANŒUVRES

THE PLAGUES
OF EGYPT

THE GLAD EYES

BAYONET
EXERCISE

YEOMEN'S LIFE IN EGYPT
(continued)

'KILL THAT FLY!'

'O THE OONT O THE OONT O THE HAIRY SCARY OONT !'
KIPLING

A SAND SHAMPOO

LETTERS TO HOME

Howard K Elcock

(By kind permission of the Editor of *The Illustrated Sporting and Dramatic News*.)

"AT NIGHT-TIDE"

When all the dalliance days of youth-time are agone,
When gladness stands usurped by pregnant fears;
  O Spirit of diviner days,
Help me to meet the leaner years!

❧

When Fate's last utterance makes the vacant chair,
And omnipresent sorrow haunts the night;
  O Spirit of diviner days,
Steel me to face the lonely fight!

❧

So stoop, when weary eyes no more may search the day
When Lethe's pall enwraps the dawn-wind's breath;
  O Spirit of diviner days,
Gird me—that I may valiantly face death!

2ND LIEUT. H. E. WHITING-BAKER.
4th BRITISH WEST INDIES RGT.

103

LETTER FROM A WOUNDED RUSSIAN SOLDIER TO HIS FAMILY

With the help of your prayers, if God be willing, I shall soon be better. But it goes without saying that when I leave Moscow I shall rejoin my regiment; that is if I am fit enough. I have to pay my debt for staying here idle for so many months, and for the suffering I have had to put up with. And if only a cold welcome is waiting for me and I am perhaps to die— well, it will have been my destiny, in which I believe. . . .

I have been examined under the X-rays. I have a bullet in my right shoulder and a piece of shrapnel in the left shoulder-blade. The bullet is behaving fairly well: as you see, I can write. But as for the piece of shrapnel, its conduct is simply revolting. Some of it has got lodged in the nerves or the muscles, and the result is that for nights and nights I have not been able to get any proper sleep. How I have cursed those Austrians!

A shell is a nice sort of customer! A bullet's nothing; you don't see it or hear it; that is to say, you hear it whistling by your ear, and once the soughing sound has passed, good-bye to it, you don't mention it again. But a shell announces its arrival with a peculiar kind of noise which I shall never forget in my life. From its whistling scream you follow its course very exactly, and you feel it coming quite close to you. At this moment you seem to lose all power of sensation; you are not afraid, but you are anxious, and expect either to be knocked down or to see your own head torn off your shoulders. Mechanically you try to duck. Then comes the explosion, and you hear cries all round you. Then, immediately after, another shell followed by another—and another.

Five or six burst by my side, and at the moment of the shock of the explosion I felt as though I had received a very heavy blow in the back. It hardly produced any pain. The experience even became quite interesting. What could have happened to me? My shoulders seemed heavy, and

I supposed that one of the shells bursting in my immediate neighbourhood had peppered me with earth and pebbles. I tried to rise, but found it was no good. I felt rather uncomfortable, and so remained lying down, although my company had gone right on ahead (we were assaulting a village). Once more I tried to get up, but I had really got it pretty badly, and my shoulders were burning. Just then my company commander came running up and took cover twenty paces from me. He looked at me with an inquiring eye, which made me ashamed. I again tried to rise, crying out to him (and a fine fool I must have looked as I did so) that something had hit me in the shoulders, but that I was annoyed and ashamed at letting my company outdistance me. I thought that the reason must have been only the merest trifle. The company commander called out to an under-officer to take command in my place and ran on, while I stayed where I was awaiting events. The shelling began again. I managed to get my pack off and thrust my head behind it. I was afraid. Supposing all of a sudden I were to be hit again ! After about five minutes I raised my head : the shells were falling farther off now. My company was right ahead of me, and a few men were stretched out round me. I happened to catch sight of my hands ; they were streaming with blood, so was my chest, and my shoulder too. "Oh !" thought I, "so I am wounded ! Then of course I can't follow my company." And this thought completely reassured me. I remained thus for some ten minutes and, the pain becoming more and more intense, I resolved to do all I could to make my way to the rear towards the ambulances. So I took my pack in my right hand and dragged myself as best I could until I was at last picked up by some stretcher-bearers who carried me to the village.

From " RIATCH."

A SHAKESPEARE TERCENTENARY IN THE TRENCHES

BY SERGEANT JOSEPH LEE, 1/4TH BATT. BLACK WATCH

THREE centuries agone since Shakespeare died,
Since he was shrouded in good English ground,
His body to the earth, his spirit free,
His bones to lie for aye, his book to live :

And here sit I, a tattered Corporal,
Reading me snatches from a tattered tome,
In fateful Flanders in a fetid trench,
While round me lie six lads in ravelled hose,
Torn kilts, and broken shoon, and lousy shirts,
Like his own Falstaff's ragged regiment.

We crouch within a dug-out's dusty depths ;
A cavern in the earth ; Adullam cave ;
A mouse's burrowing—a mole's—no more,
Yet sanctuary 'gainst the iron storm
Which works unheeded havoc o'er our heads.

Two hundred yards away the Teuton line
Twines like some scaly serpent in the grass,
Which ever and anon doth vomit fire.

And these are they would claim Will for their own ?
Well, they, if more than kin, are less than kind,
For all the day, from dawning to the dusk,
They've tried us with a dozen different deaths.

E'en so ; I turn the pages of his book
As Shakespeare turned each several folio
Of that vast, varied volumed Book of Life.

A Shakespeare Tercentenary in the Trenches

Here were stout words for cheer and 'couragement,
And it seemed England when we heard such words,
And leafy Warwick in a Morn o' May,
And Arden Forest 'neath a greenwood tree.

> This blessed plot, this earth, this realm, this England,
> This land of such dear souls, this dear, dear land;
>
> This England never did, nor never shall,
> Lie at the proud foot of a conqueror.
>
> Once more into the breach, dear friends, once more,
> Or close the wall up with our English dead!

Around us were the lodges of our dead,
Who gave their life that England still might live;
The very burrow in the which we were,
Had bones of dead men baked into the clay:
Their ghosts still seemed to linger in our lines.

But I read on; a passage from a play,
With frequent interlude and change of scene,
Till here was Denmark and the moody Dane.

Without, the Corporal did change the guard,
Even while Bernardo challenged Francisco
Upon the Battlements at Elsinore:

> FRAN. You come most carefully upon your hour.
> BER. 'Tis now struck twelve; get thee to bed, Francisco.
> FRAN. For this relief much thanks. . . .

"And so say I," said Nick, a-crawling in,
"'Tis dull work gazing into No Man's Land,
And peopling it with denizens of dream—
But do not let my coming stay the play;
The play's the thing; your audience awaits!"
So now my fingers found that sad sweet tale,
That story of that ancient grudge between
The House of Montague and Capulet.
That old-time tear, that tale of deathless love,

Made in the Trenches

Of youthful love, of love at sudden sight ;
That moonlight madness of a man and maid,
That mating in a Springtime of the world,
That Eve and Adam of a later date.
And so I read. . . .
Till o'er the sullen booming of the guns,
There rose the tumult of Verona's street,
The sounds of brawl, the bickering of blades,
And Tybalt draws upon Mercutio ;
And there is rapier play, and then, and then,
Mercutio is hurt 'neath Romeo's arm :

> MERCUTIO. A plague o' both your houses ! I am sped. . . .
> 'Tis not so deep as a well, nor so wide as a church door ; but 'tis
> enough, 'twill serve : ask for me to-morrow, and you shall find me
> a grave man. I am peppered, I warrant, for this world. A plague
> o' both your houses !

"I cry 'Amen !' to that !" upspake poor Nick,
He of reflective eye and raven hair,
"Hapsburg and Hanover ; Kaisers and Kings !—
My mood this moment is to quarrel most
With what would rob me of my life and love,
The beauty of the day, the dawn, the dusk,
And give us naught but dark, and dust, and death—
And yet, and yet, if only England live,
Our life is but a little thing to give."

And he is dead since syne ; I stood one morn,
At the chill hour of dawn, alone with—what ?
A man ?—a memory ?—a mystery ?
Which was what I had loved, and yet was not ;
Whose hand, that I had clasped so oft before,
Fell now from mine as in indifference ;
Who heard me not, who spoke not any word,
And still seemed voluble as many tongues ;
Whose eyes saw naught, yet seemed to embrace all ;
Whose lips were parted as might be in smile
That death had been so little difficult.

A Shakespeare Tercentenary in the Trenches

From the grim belt of broken, blasted trees,
There spoke the rifle of a lurking foe ;
The bullets spat upon the ruined wall
'Neath which he lay. Silence throbbed in my ear.
A bird woke in the wood, and then a wind,
Which lifted up a tress of his dark hair,
Then laid it down, like hand invisible,
And moaned like to a hungry human heart.

And there stood I, and thought of hearts would break,
And hands would move in memory 'mid that hair,
When this news reached his now unconscious home,
And I did groan for them and not for him.
I saw the dawn drift up a quiet street,
And steal into the room where he had slept ;
I heard a dog bark, and a clanging bell,
And then the kindly kitchen sounds which he
Had known on many mornings long ago.

I bent me down and felt about his breast,
And took the missives that he held so dear
From her the mistress of his ardent heart.
And they were red with his heart's blood. I found
Her pictured image, pensive smiling, sad,
As if she had foreknowledge of his fate—
And it was also showered with that red rain.
And last of all I took the little disc,
The little round that told the little round
Of his career, and it was red with blood.

I laid one kiss upon his brow, and looked
For the last time upon his sculptured face,
And so I left him, till—what comes to pass.

But here was he alive, and, " Read," says he,
" Those passages where Romeo doth part
With Juliet—and never meets her more."

CHANGES IN WHITEHALL

1914
GOING TO
ROOM 3

1916
GOING TO
ROOM 90999

ALAN. D'EGVILLE

LIEUT. A. H. D'EGVILLE,
Intelligence Corps, G.H.Q.

DENIS
COWLES

"With the Army." (2) Telling off a platoon.

HUMOROUS SIDES OF THE WAR: "WHO ARE THE PRISONERS TO-DAY?"

[An episode told in a Russian soldier's letter which shows that war is not always "frightful," and that sometimes its blackness is lit up by a flash of humour.]

OUR little detachment had been taken prisoners by the Germans. It was during the second invasion of East Prussia, at a time when our rearguards were swarming with German detachments operating separately from their main body. The prisoners had been wandering about with the Germans for some time through forests and bogs. The Germans had lost all idea of where they were, and were just moving along anyhow. They were cautiously cutting themselves a track, avoiding the slightest noise ; but they did not gain much by their precautions.

During the night we caught sight of a camp-fire, and the Germans became very elated, for according to their calculations this was bound to be a body of their own men. But they soon found out their mistake. A rifle-shot rang out, its flash spurting up in the darkness. Cries re-echoed, and then the Germans saw in front of them—Russians ! At this most unexpected encounter they had no choice but to surrender. We then found out that this other detachment of ours had also lost its way, and was wandering about aimlessly trying to find it again.

The rôles were now changed. The Russians, who a moment before had been prisoners, now took away the arms of the Germans, and we all started off once more on our voyage of discovery.

The forest seemed endless. We were marching day and night, almost without rest, and it was beginning to get on our nerves, especially the nights. We could hear gunfire in the distance, but it was impossible to know exactly which direction it was coming from.

Our common lot had reconciled us two enemies a bit ; there wasn't much difference between prisoners and captors—chiefly because both were starving, and therefore bound by the same chain. We rarely had a chance of shooting any animal. The poor beasts, driven in by the artillery fire, had crouched into the most impenetrable thickets, and if you wanted them you had to go there for them.

The adventure began to develop. Our little detachment was a sort of kernel round which two outer layers had formed— one of Germans and the other of Russians. And the whole of this band fell once more into the hands of the Germans!

When we woke up in the mornings, after those rare nights when one could get any rest, we used to ask one another, " Who are the prisoners this morning?"

Our corporal acted for us as interpreter.

This ridiculous story had its tragic side in the shape of hunger, which was becoming worse and worse. We had killed all the horses, but that did not suffice for long—there were too many mouths to feed.

We were moving along peaceably enough, without any quarrels or misunderstandings. And yet, in spite of everything, we were afraid of one another. The two sides were almost equal in numbers, or rather, I should say, they were equally feeble. Weapons in trembling hands are not of much use. It was becoming quite likely that, reduced to despair as we were, we might attack one another with teeth and nails!

The Germans were very anxious to find their own men again, but our interpreter pointed out to them that they would not gain anything by the change, as the whole of their army must be undergoing the same privations as ourselves, in this endless forest.

This adventure ended in a very unexpected way : with one accord, and without saying a word, the two groups suddenly fled in opposite directions. But the luck was with the Russians, for next day we met a friendly detachment. The corporal had brought with us a German who was terrified by the prospect of starvation. Volunteers were told off to explore the forest, and they found the whole lot of the Germans. Our " captivity " was at an end !

But the humorous side of war has its limits. This time it had passed those limits, and every single one of the men who had taken part in this comedy had to be sent into hospital, exhausted by their hunger and privations. K. T.

(Russian Army.)

"Section Five."

BY Pt J. P. EDE.
.R.A.M.C.

You may talk of the Legions of Cæsar,
  Or speak of the Grandees of Spain;
But never, I ween, when our Section is seen,
  Will you mention such rabble again.
Though a short time ago we were Civies,
  In strangely assorted attire,
Yet now, you must know, we're "some" soldiers, what ho!
  For the khaki has set us afire.

We do physical drill in the morning,
  With trousers tucked into our hose;
And with carriage erect, we produce an effect,
  All prancing around on our toes.
We fling up our hands to the Heavens,
  As though in despair or in pain,
And if there's a wretch who's omitted the "stretch"
  We do it all over again.

There's Squad Drill and Drilling with Stretchers,
  With "Changing direction, Right Form,"
When, with mixed metaphor, the Lance-Corporal will roar,
  "Don't march like a ship in a storm!"
"It's a long, long trail that's winding,"
  We scarce lift our feet at "Mark Time";
But "pick 'em up" smartly when bidden to tartly,
  And sigh for a happier clime.

" *Section Five* "

When we have finished the Drilling
  The Pioneer business begins ;
With roller or barrow, our feelings we harrow,
  And work out our penance for sins.
Yet still must we line by the Cook-house
  To carry up grub for the Hun ;
And a word in your ear, 'tis the meat tins we fear,
  For in weight they are nearly a ton.

And when the day's tasks all are ended,
  Multitudinous though they may be,
At the Sound of " Retreat " there's a scurry of feet,
  For it's football that calls us, you see.
Oh, yes ! It's a part of our training,
  And strenuous, too, you'll allow.
Then finished ? Oh, is it ! There's Exford to visit—
  Not a word on that subject. Bow wow !

Then here's to you, genial Staff Sergeant,
  Our knowledge at first was so small ;
For our faults you decry, yet with bright twinkling eye,
  And you've such funny names for us all.
Yes, you've changed us from Civies to Soldiers,
  And taught us the tricks of the trade ;
We were glad to perceive, on returning from leave,
  That Crown on the top of your braid.

A. D'E.

ACTIVE SERVICE

Up, through fresh and smiling meadows, peaceful towns, and
    woodland fair,
Up, where death lurks 'mid the shadows, or the star-shells fitful
    glare ;
Far behind, the smiling province, growing crops and chiming
    bells.
Up the line on active service in the range of German shells,
Minding not the flying metal, laughing at the mud and grime,
Buying tales of Kidd or Kettle, with the dollar and the dime.

Knowing how to conquer trouble, meeting danger with a sneer,
Coming up, and at the double, for a fight or for his beer ;
Strafing on the working parties, mocking mud-stained engineers,
Using still his " muck stick " hearty, though the war goes on
    for years.
Dying sometimes in the trenches, wounded, broken, maimed,
    or blind ;
Sun that burns or rain that drenches, none of these he seems
    to mind.

Scorning to be called a hero, hating war's unholy din,
Nerves as calm as those of Nero, time he played his violin.
In a dewy land of clover, or the city's throbbing life,
Hoping soon the war is over, there awaits his promised wife,
Fondly reading, flushed and nervous though not much his
    letter tells,
Still out on active service, dodging work and German shells.

43825, 2ND Co., C.E.

HOW ISCHAN PACHA WAS CAPTURED BY—THE DEVIL!

Our battalion, including my own company, was in pursuit of the retreating enemy. My men were marching on ahead when we ran into a couple of Turkish machine-gun sections. With a single bound half a company leapt on them, killed most of the gunners and hurled the guns into a ravine. It was a pity to waste such "trophies," but it couldn't be helped. Our fellows were knocked up as it was. I gave the order to halt, and, together with some volunteers, decided to reconnoitre the ground. Our scouting brought us to a camp which we knew later to be the camp of Ischan Pacha. So next morning, after posting my men in skirmishing order, we descended the slopes in a circle and made our way to the Turkish camp, which was on the outskirts of a wood. I told my men not to fire, as I did not want to give away our small numbers.

When we were about two hundred yards from the camp I shouted out to my fellows, "Come on, boys, follow me!" and I started running on ahead, shouting out in bad Tarbar: "Surrender! Put down your arms or I will shoot you all!" The result was extraordinary. First a Mullah came towards me, then an officer who said to me in Russian—

"Don't fire, sir. We surrender. Do not cause bloodshed!"

As soon as I had recovered from my surprise and looked at them I ascertained that they were in considerable force—more than three hundred of them, and all armed. I thought to myself that a surrender entailed certain formalities, and that I should have to disarm them; also that I had only a handful of men. They would perceive the fact. So I decided to bluff; and, approaching a general—I did not know his name—I said to him in a loud voice, "Gentlemen, you may keep your arms!" The general, whom I found out later to be the actual commander of the corps, Ischan Pacha, asked me in French—

"Who are you?"

Made in the Trenches

"Excellency, I am a captain in the Russian army, sent to you to demand your surrender. Our troops are waiting for your reply below the ridge yonder."

"In what force are you?"

"Here," I replied calmly, "behind the wood, we have one regiment; behind the ridge another regiment, and also machine-guns and artillery."

"Where are your officers?"

"Behind the ridge," I answered; and then to myself, under my breath, "I have only two corporals!"

Our conversation ended there, and I suggested that they should all mount their horses, although I had not got one myself. The Turks noticed this, and one of the general's staff asked me where my horse was. I replied carelessly—

"Behind the forest there."

On the general's order his spare horse was brought for me, and off we started, I in front and my company on the flanks and rear.

All the time that I was escorting my "booty" I kept asking myself what I should do if I fell in with a detachment of the enemy; I should not have time to take in my prisoners. However, luck favoured me. We had scarcely emerged from a gorge when I saw our artillery on the hill, which it had occupied again during the night. When we were at the bottom of the hill, and well inside our lines, I went up to the Turkish general and said to him—

"General, I have taken you prisoner with a single company!"

The Turk stood for a moment dumbfounded, and opened his eyes in a way I shall not forget for a long time, and then, putting his hand to his forehead, he uttered the words—

"You are the devil, Captain; the devil!"

CAPTAIN K.
(RUSSIAN ARMY.)

" With the Army." (3) **Derby recruit being measured for the uniform.**

(It has been the general impression that the New Armies have been weighed for their uniforms.)

"Counted for."
BY
Pte. J. P. Ede. R.A.M.C.

FIVE-AND-FIFTY sprightly lads
   Are standing on Parade,
The Section's Roll is quickly called
   And not a man has strayed.
Then five-and-fifty pairs of heels
   Together smartly click,
'Mid murmurs from admiring throngs
   " Phew ! Section Five is slick ! "

" Fall in upon your N.C.O.,"
   The order is obeyed.
(Be not alarmed, though fallen on
   He never needs First Aid.)
But he, good man, whoe'er he be,
   Assigns us each a task,
And some get light and easy jobs,
   Others—more than they ask.

Six men in deep humility,
   Before 'tis seven o'clock,
Go down on hands and knees to scrub
   Th' Administrative Block ;
For seven successive morns they writhe
   In anguish sore to see,
But on the eighth each man falls sick
   With chronic Housemaid's Knee.

"'Counted for"

A score of men are marched "two deep"
  Towards the Comp'ny's mess,
And what they find awaiting there
  Appals them, I confess,
For while the bitter wintry air
  Coagulates their blood,
They peel the epidermis
  From the soil-beladen "spud."

But five-and-fifty hungry lads
  Complete their tasks at length,
And swiftly glide to breakfast
  To recover wasted strength.
There bully beef and bacon
  They attack with frantic glee,
Or stab the sulky "submarine," [1]
  And wash it down with tea.

Many a wife in days to come,
  When strife at length is o'er,
Complacently will sit and watch
  Her hubby scrub the floor.
And as he slices carrots
  And removes potato eyes,
She'll murmur, "War is, after all,
  A blessing in disguise."

[1] A bloater.

"Light Duty."

DENIS COWLES.

MEMORIES OF GALLIPOLI

Off to the Trenches.

STIFLING A BOMB

Pruning a Sniper.

'PHEW!'

"'MORNING, HERBERT!"

"THERE GOES THE JAM!"

GUNGA DIN

H. K. ELCOCK.

SAINT PATRICK'S DAY IN THE MORNIN':

THE LOVE LILT OF CORPORAL PAT MULLOHOY OF THE
CONNAUGHT RANGERS

SAINT PATRICK'S Day in the mornin',
  A year ago to-day,
    I was a-walkin' meself alone
    Adown a green lane in ould Athlone—
    Well, sure now, of course, sweet Molly Malone
  Was with me upon the way ;
    I gathered a sprig of shamrock,
      Which in her dear breast she set,
    And, like the dew on the little plant,
      With tears her blue eyes were wet—
  For I was going away—
O, Saint Patrick's Day in the mornin',
  A year ago to-day !

Saint Patrick's Day in the mornin',
  This very blessed day,
    The ould Colonel had us all out on parade,
    And, " I'm proud of me bhoys," was what he said,
    " Ye've won fresh laurels will never fade—
  That's all that I've got to say " ;
    Then he gave us a sprig of shamrock,
      And I sent it home to my pet,
    And all that I wrote aneath it was :
      " Perhaps ye will not forget—
  For ever and alway—
Saint Patrick's Day in the mornin',
  A year ago to-day ! "

Saint Patrick's Day in the Mornin'

Saint Patrick's Day in the mornin',
  Next year this very day,
    Please God I'll be walkin' meself alone
    Adown that green lane in ould Athlone—
    With by me side sweet Molly Malone,
  To keep me upon the way ;
    Then I'll gather a sprig of shamrock,
      And set it upon her breast,
    And I'll place two kisses upon her lips—
      And I'm thinkin' ye'll guess the rest—
  For all that I'm going to say
    Is, "Ye haven't forgotten the promise ye made
  Upon Saint Patrick's Day—
Saint Patrick's Day in the mornin',
  Two years ago to-day ? "

SERGEANT JOSEPH LEE,
1/4TH BLACK WATCH.

ENCYDLOPEDIA OF MILITARY TERMS

(*Continued*)

FIX BAYONETS!—This command has caused more casualties among Drill Instructors than all the Bucking Bronchos, Bertha Barkers, or Bottled Bass than ever went to create a battle. He, the D.I., warns the squad that on the command "Fix" you must do no such thing, you must watch an unfortunate comrade who has found himself on the right of the squad. This wretched creature will, if he wishes to prevent the D.I. from having an apoplectic fit, take three paces to the front. From then on, he is the "Guiding Star." When the "man with the voice" is convinced that the G.S. has taken exactly three paces, and not two steps and a shuffle, and everything conforms with K. R. & R., and that no Rookie has grasped his entrenching tool handle (which hangs dangerously close to the bayonet), he thunders the remainder of the request, "Baynits."

At this stage of the game, the Rookie is expected to perform a physical impossibility. He must keep an eye on the man in front, and the other on the job in hand. The G.S. will then be seen to raise his left arm in a horizontal position, which is the signal that he is about to spring to attention and back up.

NOTE.—To any one in Group 909 who might read this, I have some cheerful news for you. You, like the rest of us, are fed up with fixing bayonets by numbers; well, when you get out here your bayonet troubles will be over. A generous Government has seen to it that we have all kinds of them. There is the bright one for Fritz, another for toasting, one for poking the brazier, one for opening tins of peaches, one for scraping the mud from one's boots, bread, puttees, etc. One for a candlestick, one for manicuring purposes and a hundred and one other things.—From *The Listening Post*.

SKETCHES FROM FLANDERS

Lieut. A. H. D'Egville,
Intelligence Corps, G.H.Q.

A HINT TO SPECULATORS.

"Joe, 'as it ever struck you that this would be one of the places where Tubes would pay?"

128

HALF AN HOUR ON THE PARADE GROUND:

Or, Why I am so Popular with my Platoon

"Ah, good mornin', Sergeant, good mornin'. Good mornin', platoon. Nice day for a little frill—drill, I mean, what! So you think the platoon is tired of drill, do you, Sergeant? I don't. That settles it, doesn't it?

"Well, don't stand there like a musical comedy hero. Get 'em dressed and 'shunned, and all that. I'm goin' to inspect 'em, I am. Now then, my lads, just try and think I'm a general—I may be some day, you know. What did you say? Nothin'? Well, don't say it again. Stick your tummies out and your chests in—I mean t'other way—and try and look like real soldiers, even if you aren't. Look at *me*, my lads, look at *me*! Try and copy me.

"What the ——! Why the ——! My dear, *good* fellows, what on *earth* are you all doin'? You look as if you'd all been suddenly gassed. Brace your knees up, and don't squint. Sergeant Tomkins! Step this way, please. Now just look at *your* platoon. Do you mean to tell me you've been drillin' this platoon on and off for four months and you haven't been able to lick 'em into better shape than that? 'Shun 'em and dress 'em. I say, dress 'em and 'shun 'em, or whatever you call it.

"That's better. Now then, we'll inspect. Wait a minute, Sergeant; allow *me* to give the word of command *sometimes*. Thank you. H'm, h'm——. My platoon! For inspection—stand at—ease! Very good, very good. What did you say, Sergeant? At attention? I disagree with you; I disagree with you *en*tirely. I am not a hard taskmaster, and there's nothing that pains me more than to see a whole lot of wretched blighters standin' about like a lot of bally nine-pins. Don't you agree with me, you fellows, what?

"There you are, Sergeant, what did I tell you! Silence gives consent, you know.

I

"No, don't follow me round like a faithful hound. You go round the pit, while I go round the stalls.

"Now we shall see what we shall see. Aha! what's this? A golden hair upon thy shoulder-strap, Jenkins! Oh, Jenkins! O thou *gay* old dog, Jenkins! Hast in sooth wimped yestre'en? Wined and wimped, what? I did not think 'twas in thee, thou saucy sinner. Now then, Smith, what's the joke? Sergeant Tomkins, put Private Smith on fatigue for a month.

"Ha, here we have old Simpson. How's the missus, eh? Very well, is she; that's good. Any addition to the family recently? No? Bad luck. Never say die.

"Well, well; not a single dirty button. That does me credit, hey, Sergeant, don't it?

"Will I inspect rifles? What, poke my eye down the tube and all that? Ha, ha, not much! There might be a bullet or bomb or something. Supposin' one of the beastly things were to explode where would I be, eh?

"Ah, you may well shrug your shoulders. No, no; when I was a small boy, Sergeant, I was always told never to point my pop-gun at anybody. Do you think I'm goin' to let anybody point these beastly things at me? I may *look* a silly ass, but I'm not, you know. What did you say? Nothin'? Extraordinary habit you have of sayin' nothin'.

"Doesn't it strike you, Sergeant, that you've been wastin' a hell of a time talkin'? When I say I want to drill the platoon I jolly well mean it, you know. You toddle back to your place now, like a good chap and don't forget to shave to-morrow. What did you say? You *have* shaved this mornin'? Glad to hear it, 'm sure. I never said you hadn't, did I?

"Now then, platoon—please listen, that man with the carbuncle on his nose—when I give the word, 'As you were,' I want you to understand that you've got to *be* as you were, that is, as you were before you were what you were last. Got me? Now then, are you ready? One—two—three. As you were!

"I thought so—I *thought* so! Not the faintest idea how to drill. Sergeant, hither! Now look at 'em—look at 'em,

Half an Hour on the Parade Ground

I say. Have you ever in your life—eh? What? Don't whisper man, don't whisper. Speak up. 'Gettin' them all of a muck,' d'ye say? Muck? *Muck?* What d'ye mean, sir? Don't you dare call my men 'muck,' sir! As fine a body of men, sir, as you'll find anywhere—not barrin' the Guards. I'll have you court-martialled, 'pon me soul, I will. No explanations—I won't listen, damme, I won't, I won't! Lend me a pair of scissors somebody! I'll stripe you of your strips, 'pon me soul I will. No—go away. Get back to your place before I lose my temper.

"Now then, platoon, let's get to work. 'Shun! As you were. 'Shun! As you were. About turn! As you were. Stand at—'shun! Aha! I had you there. You *thought* I was going to say 'ease,' didn't you? But I didn't, did I? Conclusion, or, as one might say, moral—'Don't think.' No soldier ever thinks, you know. Great game, what! Suits me down to the ground.

"Well, well, what else can we do to make the fleeting hours flit, eh? I know—bright idea.

"Platoon—'shun! Quick march! Very nice too. About turn! Left—left—left—about turn! Left—left—left—about turn! What a game! About turn! This is splendid. About turn. Ha, ha, what a life we lead, don't we! About turn! Oh, I'm getting fed up, I am. Hi, whoa! Halt! or whatever you call it.

"Sergeant Tomkins, just you—er just carry on and all that, you know. Yes, drill 'em a bit. Now I've given you the cue, you see the kind of thing I want, what? No, I'm off for a drink, I am.

"Bye-bye, platoon! What a life!"

SCOTTIE.
(From *The Gasper*.)

OFF TO BLIGHTY!

Parody: "OFF TO PHILADELPHIA."

My name is Private Mears,
Of the Nineteenth Fusiliers,
  And the side of all the Boches I'm a thorn in.
Soon in other ranks you'll find me,
And the pals I leave behind me
  When they hear the news will all go into mournin'.

  With my pack upon my shoulder,
  Faith, there's no man could be bolder,
    Though I'm leaving now the Corps that I was
      born in,
  But I've lately got the notion
  That I ought to seek promotion,
    So I'm buzzing off to Blighty in the mornin'.

It's farewell to Minnie-Werfer
(If I come back I'll deserve her)
  And the mud my little dug-out floor adornin'.
Life out here is just a query,
So I'm feeling mighty cheery,
  For I'm off for a commission in the mornin'.

  With my pack, etc.

When they told me I could leave the place
I tried to keep a solemn face,
  To show it gave me pleasure I was scornin'.
But *someday* I'll get promotion,
And come back across the ocean
  To my dug-out in the trenches—in the mornin'.

  With my pack, etc.

STROZZI.
(From *The Gasper*.)

THROUGH A SENTRY'S EYES

MANY opportunities have been given me to observe the various types of humanity that go to make up our Armies ; for I have been stationed on five different road posts in as many different places. They were spread over only two months, but they were the most eventful of any of the year 1915—August and September. As the stations varied from ten miles behind the trenches to within half a mile of them, I was enabled to obtain a comprehensive grasp of all the preparations leading up to the Loos attack.

The first signs that the English were about to make a big offensive came when, in conversation with some gunners, we learned of all the guns that were being concentrated. Then we began to notice that vacant positions were being occupied, and soon it seemed as if it were not possible to find room for the artillery of all calibres that arrived ; and yet more came every day.

From now onwards the preparations appeared to take a more active air, and all roads became a stream of wagons loaded with coils of barbed wire, wagons of direction boards and trench boards, wagons of fodder, limbers of ammunition and covered lorries that might contain any wonderful secret one could imagine for defeating the Germans. The roads were occupied either with this stream of loads or else with the empty vehicles returning from the "Front," according to whether they were "Up" or "Down" traffic ways. Oh yes, careful routes were mapped out ; and dire penalties were threatened to all using them in any other direction than that indicated. It is really astonishing how angry a man can become when, at midnight, you quietly but firmly tell him that the road is barred and he must go two or three extra miles by a roundabout route. Really, I have often felt relieved to remember that Chaplains are not in the habit of prowling around at that hour ! Nearly every one who has spent some time on "posts" has had the pleasant experience of turning back a General. Mine was a mere Brigadier, but the corporal who insisted on diverting the Corps Commander from his path was rewarded with promotion : one more illustration of " Unto him that hath shall be given."

As if the Fates were anxious that I should see the fulfilment of all these preparations, I was placed on a post very close to the trenches during the attack. I was here for a week before and a week after the 25th of September ; during the fortnight, soldiers of every rank and kind passed. Our " friends across the way " greeted our arrival with a quantity of shelling that did much damage. A dozen houses were severely battered ; one at a corner had the whole façade dispersed, leaving a view of hanging floors and broken furniture. Many men later figured in the casualty lists through the day's shelling at that one point. A Colonel was among the victims ; the village baker was killed at his own doorstep : I saw his wife being led away in an hysterical condition, and her shrieks were pitiful to hear.

For some days afterwards the sentry at my post became quite important : officers consulted him as to the safety of passing the danger-point. A white-haired Colonel of Artillery, and a Major, who seemed quite concerned about it, were my most exalted questioners. I remember that after hearing a couple of 6-inchers explode in rapid succession a figure came flying round the bend from the village, on a bicycle, and hastily dismounted by my side, presumably as the only human being in sight. He was a young, fresh-faced Lieutenant, and breathlessly proceeded to tell me of his narrow escape, showing me a tear in his breeches caused by a piece of shell.

Close to the firing line as it was, officers were still the comrades of the men, and had not yet dropped the spirit of camaraderie of the trenches for the aloofness demanded by dis-cipline in the rear. An officer had occasion to wait near me for a man who had fallen out from his platoon ; this was a few nights after the Loos attack. There, in the bright moonlight, we chatted for five minutes as if we had known each other for years. On another occasion I enjoyed a similar chat with an officer in the R.M.A., who seemed to carry the atmosphere of a quiet London club.

Another officer, this time in charge of Battalion Transport, caused me some slight amusement. I had told him some order that affected him, when he looked down on me from his horse and said, " Yes, yes, Sentry. I am quite willing to obey orders, but why can't I pass here on horseback ? This wagon can "— pointing to a G.S. wagon I had just challenged and allowed to pass ; " it's larger, and makes more noise than I do."

" Orders, sir."

" I know ; but why have they made the order ? what's the reason ? "

Then my grin was wide ; I could only reply, " The Army, sir "—and comprehension dawned on him.

A comrade had the pleasure of listening to a well-known poet, in the ranks, discourse on the moon, the stars, and the birds ; while we all had a long chat with a famous V.C., who was soon afterwards killed. For nearly two hours was this hero shot at, bombed, and shelled, never to be touched ; then, one night he crept " over the top " to hunt for souvenirs, and a chance bullet gave him his death-wound. Such is the irony of fate.

Not all the passers-by were as pleasant to see as these. There came a morning when a passing officer warned us to have our gas-helmets ready, when every gun within sight and hearing spat death as fast as it could. Then, later on, there passed a few men with bandaged limbs or heads—scouts of a vast army that flowed by all day and most of the next. The attack had begun ; Loos had fallen. The news was great and good ; therefore, despite their wounds, these fellows laughed and joked, smoked and were happy. To some we were able to render a few services ; one wanted to light his cigarette, but his right hand was useless ; another, for the same reason, could not get to his pocket ; to others we gave water. Some came by with their clothes in rags ; one poor fellow seemed to have his back all scratched by barbed wire. Friends went by, and from these we obtained an idea how the fight was progressing ; the corporal's brother passed, with a bullet through the wrist ; a few staggered along, and were helped by comrades less seriously wounded.

One night three figures approached us ; they turned out to be an injured member of a distinguished regiment being helped by two comrades. Invited into our billet they rested awhile, and a passing "Linseed Lancer" pronounced it a broken rib. I searched high and low in the dark for a dressing station, but one was not to be found. I had to stop half a dozen motor ambulances before one was discovered with a vacancy for a "lying case."

Into the quiet and peace of our little group an impetuous Staff officer projected himself one evening, and disorder reigned for a short time. He wanted to read our orders. There had been a complaint. The N.C.O. handed him the bunch, which he snatched, letting some flutter to the ground. The important one was missing—it was afterwards found in the grate. He violently upbraided the corporal, flung himself into his car, and sped away, leaving us all with the impression that we were lucky not to have been all put under close arrest.

British Tommies were not the only men we saw; a good many French soldiers passed us also. Regularly each morning, for several days, a dull yellow car drew up by my side and out stepped a short, waddling Major and a tall young Staff Captain of the French Army. Both wore the shrapnel-proof helmets, for they were on a visit to the French trenches close by. The senior officer sported a most extraordinary uniform, half a dozen shades of khaki, with a large helmet pressing on his ears, and pince-nez balanced on his fat little nose—the whole effect was most comical. A picturesque figure was the Colonel of a Colonial regiment, dressed in the sky-blue uniform, his cheerful face adorned with a long white beard, wearing the large tam-o'-shanter of his regiment, and astride a magnificent white charger. He was a splendid picture of vigorous old age. More than one French General passed us ; I believe one was the famous General Foch.

I narrowly missed being publicly embraced by a couple of enthusiastic *Poilus* ; as it was I felt quite embarrassed. One of them proudly showed me a copy of his regimental orders, mentioning him for bravery in rescuing wounded under fire ; nothing would satisfy him until I had read it out to my comrades.

It has also been our pleasure to give breakfast or some other meal to a few stragglers. We obtained our first connected account of the Loos fight from two typical members of the

15th Division, who had been right up to the Cité St. Auguste, and they described the retirement from that place very graphically.

On Saturday evening, September 25th, a few civilian refugees from Loos came past, with their personal effects on a cart; one was a picturesque old man with a flowing white beard, another was the "heroine of Loos"—Emilienne Moreau.

We had other visitors whose presence was not so welcome— the shells of our kindly enemy. One night they started dropping high explosive along the road at the same moment that some artillerymen near by were unloading a day's supply of ammunition—we were not sorry when both lots of shells were out of the way. It is not very pleasant, either, when an 8-in. howitzer shell drops in the nearest house. When three "morning greetings" are placed in rapid succession, 80 yards off, you wonder sometimes if the next three will be 80 yards nearer. An excited Frenchman brought us a bomb he had found on the railway; once it was in our hands nothing would persuade him to take it back. We most earnestly assured him that if he would only dig a hole in the earth and bury it, or leave it in a pail of water, all would be well; it was no good, he merely waved his arms, shrugged his shoulders, and walked rapidly away. Left with it on our hands, we were nearly as nervous as he was; none of us were bombers, and there have been so many accidents with bombs. A corporal, fresh from England, was starting to pull at certain knobs and levers, when he was hastily relieved of his burden—it merely confirmed us in our opinion of him. Finally, we wrapped the thing in paper, placed it on a bank, retired to a safe distance, and allowed a "crack" shot to "pot" at it; at the third shot something happened; it was not exactly an explosion, but we only found the white metal cap when we went to investigate.

Such are some of the incidents that enliven the monotony of road guards, and very thankful for them we are.

"CYCLIST."

THE "WORKING PARTY."

(A dirge by Bill.)

THEN again said "Hiawatha"
I am hugely interested
In this working party business.
Should you ask me who discovered
And commenced this form of torture,
I would tell you in a jiffy.
It was not the Brigade Major
Or a Company Commander,
'Twasn't Victor of Vancouver
(Who commands this here battalion),
Wasn't any one with feelings,
You can bet your dollar ten per.
'Twas a special friend of "Wilhelm's"
Who receives his correspondence
Where the conscientious shirkers
Toil and labour at his fires,
(Cashed-in with the mumps and measles
And such ladylike diseases),
Shovelling coal to beat the devil
To torment themselves for ever.
(You can *guess* the map location.)

Full of patriotic spirit,
We came out to fight the Boches,
Blast their hides and damn their whiskers.
Now the greater part of Belgium
Is contained in bags, sand, common
Through the energetic efforts
Of the ever-ready "Seventh."
Should you meet a column, moving
Single file, and stretched out snake-wise,

138

The "Working Party"

Loaded down with stake and wire,
Shovels, picks, and Susie's sand-bags,
Mortar bombs, expanded metal,
Newton Pippin's detonators,
Mills grenades and other "bangos,"
Cruising slowly 'twixt the shell holes
(Using language not atrocious)
On a night as dark as Hades—
Cloud-bursts bursting from the heavens
With enthusiastic fervour—
No great intellect's required
To identify the unit,
We have been there and we've had some—
"Pass the Seventh."

Mortars, trench, are mostly useful
When there's no retaliation.
Picks and shovels have their uses—
Sentries not on duty notice.
Stakes and wire and Susie's sand-bags
Built by our Black Art exponent,
Are most excellent as targets,
And the Boche esteems them highly,
Bashes them in high good-humour,
And "Kr-r-r-umps" the work of hours.
So the merry war continues
And we're satisfied to be here.

Now, a word to you "objectors,"
Cranks and peace talk agitators,
Who corrupt the air in Blighty.
"Safety first" and no conscription
Will not beat the Boche in Flanders,
Which is our immediate business.
We will *do* our working parties,
Grouse and growl but get the work done,
Whilst *your* maiden manhood grovels
At the prospect of a duty

Made in the Trenches

Which should be your highest privilege.
Those who murmur " Gott Strafe England,"
As they sight along their barrels,
Have their *own* Gods—what have you got ?
Damn *your* hide and blast *your* whiskers,
And just wait till *this* is over.

Working parties are the devil,
And we grant you that most freely ;
We could use *you* if you'd venture,
In the meantime we'll continue
At this unpleasant pastime,
And the knowledge that we've done so
When at last we're ticked for—Hades ?
(Where all good old Seventh go to)
Will not make us lie uneasy
And alone, before our fellows.

W. A. C.
(From *The Listening Post*.)

(from a letter) "We can always have a good "Wash" in the Trenches" J.MAC

TOLD IN A DUG-OUT

In a London hospital a wounded Irish soldier was relating his extraordinary adventures to a party of lady visitors. After a vivid reconstruction of the fight in which he knocked out seventeen Huns and a machine-gun "wid me wan hand alone begob," he concluded "an that's the end of the shtory. The surgeons took me and laid me for all as though I was dead in an ammunition wagon."

"Oh, but you don't mean an ammunition wagon, my good man, you mean an ambulance wagon," interrupted one of the fair visitors.

"Sorra a bit," he replied sadly. "Shure, I was so filled with bullets they decided I ought to go in the ammunition wagon."

.   .   .   .   .

A newly formed company of a Lancashire battalion was under the vocal fire of a red-faced drill sergeant. For hours he had roared and raved and used up all the vernacular in the English language. Towards the end of the afternoon his commands grew more and more rapid and involved.

" 'Shun !" he yelled.

The company froze with fright.

"Left turn !"

About fifty per cent. turned with an air of indecision, then, before the rest could follow, he cried in quick succession—

"Right turn ! About turn ! Quick march ! Halt !"

He glared in disgust at the extraordinary result, and started with surprise as one yokel left the rank and made for the barrack-room.

"Hi, you !" he roared. "Where the devil are you off to ?"

The youth turned and looked at him pityingly.

"Aye, and it's real sick of it I am, an' all," he drawled. "Thou doesn't kna tha own mind for two minutes together."

1st Private : " Say !   Have you heard that Ted Smith has got the D.C.M. ? "

2nd Private : " What for ? "

1st Private : " I dunno."

2nd Private : " Blimy, why ain't I got one too ?   I hid in the same dug-out."

·   ·   ·   ·

After one of the advances in the recent big push, a party of English soldiers were told off to bury the German dead. While they were thus engaged one of the burial party suddenly called out—

" Hi ! Sergeant !   Here's a bloke wot says 'e ain't dead. What shall I do with 'im ? "

The sergeant spat contemptuously.

" Can't believe a word they say," he replied.   " They're all born liars.   If he says he's dead you can bet he's alive.   If he says he's alive you can take it he's dead—better put him in."

·   ·   ·   ·   ·

Everybody in the army seems to have heard the story of Private J. B., the truth of which is vouched for as army stories invariably are.

Private J. B. was doing his first " guard " outside a regimental depot.   He had only joined up a week or so previous, and the task was awe-inspiring.   To make matters worse, all that afternoon the sergeant had come out from the guard-room at frequent intervals to inquire if the Colonel had come in yet ; to which Private J. B. replied in a mechanical negative, since he didn't know the Colonel from Adam.   Towards the evening an insignificant little man approached, and, stopping, looked at the sentry sternly.

" Why don't you salute me ? " he said wrathfully.   " Don't you know who I am ?   I'm the Colonel, sir—the Colonel."

A smile spread over the features of the sentry.

" Oh, you're 'im, are you ! " he replied.   " I've been looking for you all the afternoon.   You won't 'arf cop out ; the sergeant's been arsting all over the shop for you."

·   ·   ·   ·   ·

Told in a Dug-out

A little fat soldier crept along the muddy, battered trench. He wasn't a bit afraid, but the sensation was new, and he was obviously a little nervy.

"What's the range to the enemy's front trench?" he asked.

"You've been told once," said the corporal. "Two hundred."

"Two hundred!" he muttered reflectively. "Two hundred."

There was a slight pause.

"And how far back is our next trench?"

"What's that to do with it?"

"Well, how far anyway?"

"Oh, about a hundred yards."

"One hundred! One hundred."

He polished up the foresight of his rifle with his finger and smiled contentedly.

"That's all right," he muttered.

The corporal looked at him curiously.

"What do you mean by 'that's all right'?"

"Oh, nothing. I was only thinking it would take a damn good German to give me fifty yards in the hundred and win."

G. G.

THE BARRICADE

From a trench whose number doth end in one,
There runs a road, or there used to run,
Up 'twixt the trees to a Belgium Town,
And this is the road the Huns came down.

Down the road at their own sweet will,
With never a shot to stay or kill—
At least they did in the days gone by,
The good old days they recall with a sigh.

When the 5th and 10th, and 7th too,
Did mighty deeds as all men knew ;
For didn't they tell us in communiques
That never varied for weeks and weeks,

How an officer with a bomb or two
(This is the way the story grew)
Went out with a man on either hand
And strafed the Hun, from " No Man's " land.

But after a time they wearied of war,
And begged relief from the C. M. R.
Poor beggars who didn't know the way,
To fight the Huns with words that flay,

But hung on to the swelter of mud and stench,
Called by the 2nd Brigade a trench,
And did their bit with such a vim,
That Fritzie wondered what happened to him.

Had he not used for months gone by,
A listening post, snug, warm and dry,
Convenient, too, to the British wire,
Quite unmolested by hostile fire.

The Barricade

But all had changed when the C. M. R.,
    Quite unversed in the rules of war,
Imagined whenever they saw a Hun,
    'Twas time and place to use a gun.

The rifles ring, the machine guns roar,
    The listening post rests safe no more,
But in a hurry with pick and spade,
    Erected the famous Barricade.

The Barricade, 'twixt you and me,
    Was nothing more than a cut-down tree,
A little mud, a stone or two,
    But, oh dear me, how it grew and grew.

In Bulford Camp, where the warriors lay
    Who had strafed the Huns in such a way,
That Fritz, by nature a timid wight,
    Walked down the road in broad daylight.

The yarn was told that the Barricade
    Would cost the lives of a whole Brigade,
And they hurried up, those stalwart men,
    Eager to face the foe again.

Colonels two, of Majors a score,
    Captains and Subalterns galore,
A thousand men and a ration of rum,
    To take the Barricade away from the Hun.

The Gunners lent a helping hand,
    In fact, they were the whole d——d band,
They blew the Barricade sky-high
    And left poor Fritzie high and dry.

Then the gallant boys of the 2nd Brigade
    Hopped over, and oh what a noise they made !
They captured a corpse and a senseless Hun,
    A bomb, some wire, and a rusty gun.

Made in the Trenches

And returned in triumph, those dashing men,
  And killed the Hun again and again,
And published the news both far and wide,
  Then hurried back to their Q.M.'s side.

Indent, said they, so all may know
  How we have earned a D.S.O.,
A cross or two, a D.C.M.,
  A mention in despatch, "Pro Tem."

And now again peace reigneth deep,
  They never rouse the Hun from sleep,
But sit and dream, in those trenches far,
  And no longer slam the C. M. R.

C. M. R.

(From *The Listening Post*.)

"Hi! Jock—they're stealing your cake!"
(From *The Searchlight*.)

"A LONELY SOLDIER"

A Warning to Others

IT was during a short rest in billets "Somewhere in France" that Lance-Corporal X., of No. 13 Platoon, made the important discovery that he was lonely. Lonely soldiers have my sympathy, and as I had a grievance against Lance-Corporal X.—he was the man responsible for the dividing of my section's rations—I persuaded him to insert a notice to the effect of his loneliness in his local paper.

A week later the following illuminating paragraph appeared in the columns of the *Slumpton Daily News* :—

LONELY SOLDIER.—Gentleman ranker, age 22, would welcome cheery letters from members of the opposite sex, age 19–23. Photos welcome.

Then followed the address. A few days later the regimental postman brought with him, in addition to the company's letters, 48 postcards, 131 letters, and 39 parcels, all for our lonely lance-corporal. The following day there was a considerable falling-off in the number of effeminate effusions, and I helped the Lonely One to acknowledge most of the epistles, informing the senders of his gratitude, and enclosing his kind regards. The letters were interesting, amusing, and pathetic, as may well be expected. One sympathizer wrote :—

MY DEAR LONELY HERO,

How I should like the privilege of making you feel happier and less lonely! I am very pretty, aged twenty, and extremely modest. Dad is on the Town Council, a churchwarden, and a member of the Local Tribunal, while I am on the local committee of the "Help us to Help Others League." Good-bye, my brave and lonely soldier.

Ever yours,

PRISCILLA ARMITAGE.

PS.—The Vicar would be shocked if he knew!

We passed on from Priscilla, as she had omitted to enclose her photograph. One fair correspondent enclosed a couple of lines, which ran as follows :—

My name's Pamela, be it known ; so popular I am,
To all the boys for miles around I'm simply known as " Pam."

Hers was the prettiest photograph in the lot, but, unfortunately, on the other side of it was an advertisement of somebody's dental cream ! Lance-Corporal X. just said one word. The fact that I am a member of the Wesleyan persuasion prevents me from mentioning it here, but it rhymed with the rest of the verse all right.

Another ambitious correspondent enclosed a photograph of Miss Gladys Cooper, although it certainly bore the signature, " Yours, Daisy." She was ambitious, without a doubt, and deserved to get on, or off, as the case may be.

As letters continued to arrive in twenties, we came to the conclusion that Lance-Corporal X. was no longer lonely, and I suggested that he might remedy matters by removing the notice setting forth his loneliness, which was still appearing in the local press. This he accordingly did, and our clerical labour was somewhat relieved. It was impossible for a single soldier, however lonely, to correspond with 439 different young ladies, so we eventually decided upon one pretty brunette of twenty summers and nineteen winters—Mabel Beaumont by name—with whom he regularly corresponded. He sent her a German helmet, and their Platonic friendship turned to what the cynics describe as " love." Her notepaper was liberally sprayed with blots and eau-de-Cologne, and sealed with kisses and gummed labels, whilst the letters of Lance-Corporal X. kept the Company censor fully occupied.

They continued to correspond with each other until the Lonely One was wounded. He was sent to England, where he spent many weeks nursing a wounded arm in a Northern hospital, while " she " was nursing a wounded heart in her own home. When he was finally discharged from hospital he went straight to the town where his fair correspondent resided—straight to see the maiden of his choice. But alas ! Misfortunes never come singly. The photo which he carried in the left breast-pocket of his tunic, in close proximity to his heart, proved to be a photograph of his widowed correspondent's niece ! Vile woman. Base deceiver !

Still, Lance-Corporal X. was a returned hero, and every one knows that heroes are made of the right kind of stuff. He soon met the niece at a whist drive. She met him on the following night ; then they continued to meet each other. (He always did believe in meeting trouble half-way.) They went to the " pictures " regularly each week—that, of course, was before the amusements tax—and for eighteen weeks they never saw a picture. Chaplin films passed by unnoticed while she learned to call him Leslie.

Now this kind of thing cannot go on for ever, as the cinema attendant said when he switched on his electric lamp, and in course of time she, like her wicked aunt, proved to have very little respect for her hero. The wretch ! She married him !

Luckily for me, Lance-Corporal X. never returned to the front, although he signed on again when his time expired. Most married men do—and I don't blame them either !

N.B.—The author is not necessarily of the opinion that all lonely soldiers who correspond with lonely marriageable daughters will meet with the same fate as Lance-Corporal X., but he certainly thinks they deserve it.

H. E. GOFTON.

An awkward moment.

THE CONVOY

THE sunny rose of autumn's smoky day
    Had almost fled. The chill was in the air,
When issued forth from Gaspé's smiling bay
    A grand Armada, 'neath a cruiser's care;
A great and grand flotilla, speeding forth
    Beneath the oily pall of clinging smoke—
A gift to Motherland, of priceless worth—
    Th' Atlantic's lazy swells to life awoke.

Thrice ten and two great modern Argosies,
    That hurried to the Field, the best of youth
To bear their country's colours o'er the seas,
    And herald Canada to national growth.
Great sons of sires whose willing blood has given
    To our New World the sterling of the Old;
Most worthy volunteers are these, undriven
    To take up arms; freemen, but strong and bold.

Beneath the watching escort's wakeful eyes
    The fleet pulsed on. The ocean's lazy roll
Bore three long straggling lines, 'neath low'ring skies,
    Spread as a flock of geese cleave toward their goal.
Thrice ten and two great sullen merchantmen,
    As, sullen in their cloaks of drab and black,
They freighted over thrice ten thousand souls.
    How many of these same may they bring back?

The Convoy

The days roll by. The ocean slowly yields
  Its bosom to the squadron's steady pace,
Until the cliffs of England rise to greet
  The scions of her colonizing race
Come home—to give their all. Come home—to fight.
  Come home—though born of that far western land
Where Britain's shield is 'stablished for the right,
  They volunteered to lend an armed hand.

Oh ! Plymouth, cradle of the mighty Drake ;
  The haven of his vessels' hopes and fears ;
Yet have you ever seen so fine a sight ?
  Or have you ever waked to such a crest of cheers
As roars aboard the transports, on whose decks
  Are packed the khaki hosts ? Has e'er a day
Such wealth of loyal blood, such willing hands
  Brought to your shores ?
All England answers—" Nay ! "

Late SERGT. FRANK S. BROWN, P.P.C.L.I.
(From The Iodine Chronicle.)

THINGS WE MAY HOPE TO SEE—

1. An Orderlette carrying her own milk-can.

2. An Orderlim commended by a Sister for general proficiency and good conduct.

3. A Visitor who knows the way to D Wards.

4. A work of undoubted merit by a member of Hut 6.

5. A Patient whose "Blues" fit him.

6. A minist'ring Angel smoothing the pillow of a wounded hero. (With acknowledgments to Harold B-gb-e.)

7. A Non-com. doing something.

8. A member of the staff who is contented with his job. (He is marked with a cross, X.)

PTE. STEPHEN DE LA BERE
(From *The 3rd London General Hospital Gazette.*)

153

POEMS OF LIFE AND DEATH

❥

SONNETS OF TWILIGHT AND YOUTH[1]

I

VISION.

CHARMED with the ceaseless music of the brook—
Babbling with hope and with Youth's deathless song;
Full with the joys of lovers who sans book
Have found that happiness is just to long
For some sweet face, some voice, some footstep known,
But better still to feel some ardent press
Of lips that are with peerless passion blown,
Mad for the magic of a deathless kiss—

Charmed with the sound and what it bears to me
From out the distance of the unborn years
I weep—O pinewood shadows chilling me
With shadow-haunted grief, presage of tears !
Must youth whose orient wings are lightning-plumed
Be crowned with grief, to sure death be doomed ?

II

SHADOW.

O why should Youth, whose symbol is the lark
That mounts with new-born dreams unto the sky,
Be doomed at frequent intervals to lie
Voiceless and dreamless, prostrate in the dark ?
Why 'mid the laughter of the carnival,
The feast of roses sensuous with delight,
Why should there break the terror of a call—
Death calling Youth into the unknown night ?

[1] Corporal Streets, in submitting these sonnets some months ago, wrote : " They express not only my feelings but the feelings of thousands of others who, like myself, are on the verge of departure from England."

For thus at morn the twilight-footed Death
Sweeps from the zenith to the orient rim
Where Youth doth play : and soon his phantom wreath
Fadeth like beauty into distance dim :
Fadeth like yon rich sunset in the sky,
That seems O sad and tenderly to die !

III

CHALLENGE.

Go tell yon shadow stalking 'neath the trees
With silent-footed terror, go tell Death
He cannot with Life's vast uncertainties
Affright the heart of Youth ! For Youth cometh
With flush of impulse, passion to defeat,
Undaunted purpose, vision clear descried,
To counteract, lay at Death's unseen feet
The gauntlet of defiance. Far and wide,
Beyond the fear of that unknown exile,
That brim of Time, that web of darkness drawn
Across Life's orient sky, there breaks a smile
Of light that swells into the hope of dawn :
A dream within the dark, like evening cool,
Like sunset mirror'd in yon darken'd pool.

IV

TRIUMPH.

Thus dreaming in the shadows of the pines,
Feeling the presage of the unborn years,
I know that Youth will brave the dark confines
And wrest from Death his diadem of fears.
I know that should I still and prostrate lie
Amid Death's harvest there on Belgium's plain
No false regret shall scorning wander by
And taunt me that my Youth hath been in vain.

155

Made in the Trenches

Rather in my last moments will I live
My life's past purpose rich in destiny,
Its scorn of Ease, its eagerness to give
Challenge to all blind to eternity.
Death will not, cannot wrest from out my mind
The thought that Love its life in death can find.

GALLIPOLI

Upon the margin of a rugged shore
There is a spot now barren, desolate,
A place of graves, sodden with human gore
That Time will hallow, Memory consecrate.
There lie the ashes of the mighty dead,
The youth who lit with flame Obscurity,
Fought true for Freedom, won through rain of lead
Undying fame, their immortality.
The stranger wand'ring when the war is over,
The ploughman there driving his coulter deep,
The husbandmen who golden harvests reap—
From hill and ravine, from each plain and cover,
Will hear a shout, see phantoms on the marge,
See men again making a deathless charge.

This sequence of poems was submitted for publication with the following letter :—

"They were inspired while I was in the trenches, where I have been so busy that I have had little time to polish them. I have tried to picture some thoughts that pass through a man's brain when he dies. I may not see the end of the poems, but hope to live to do so. We soldiers have our views of life to express, though the boom of death is in our ears. We try to convey something of what we feel in this great conflict to those who think of us, and sometimes, alas! mourn our loss. We desire to let them know that in the midst of our keenest sadness for the joy of life we leave behind we go to meet death grim-lipped, clear-eyed, and resolute-hearted."—[Ed.]

YOUTH'S CONSECRATION

Lovers of Life, dreamers with lifted eyes,
O Liberty, at thy command we challenge Death !
The monuments that tell our fathers' faith
Shall be the altars of our sacrifice.
Dauntless we fling our lives into the van,
Laughing at death, because within Youth's breast
Flame lambent fires of Freedom ; man for man
We yield to thee our heritage, our best.
Life's highest product, youth exults in Life ;
We are Olympian gods in consciousness ;
Mortality to us is sweet, yet less
We value Ease when Honour sounds the strife.
Lovers of Life, we pledge thee Liberty
And go to death calmly, triumphantly !

LOVE OF LIFE

Reach out thy hands, thy spirit's hands, to me
And pluck the youth, the magic from my heart—
Magic of dreams whose sensibility
Is plumèd like the light ; visions that start
Mad pressure in the blood ; desire that thrills
The soul with mad delight : to yearning wed
All slothfulness of life ; draw from its bed
The soul of dawn across the twilight hills.
Reach out thy hands, O spirit, till I feel
That I am fully thine ; for I shall live
In the proud consciousness that thou dost give,
And if thy twilight fingers round me steal
And draw me unto death—thy votary
Am I : O Life, reach out thy hands to me !

157

AN ENGLISH SOLDIER

He died for love of race ; because the blood
Of northern freemen swelled his veins ; arose
True to tradition that like mountain stood
Impregnable, crown'd with its pathless snows.
When broke the call, from the sepulchred years
Strong voices urged and stir'd his soul to life ;
The call of English freemen fled his fears
And led him (their true son) into the strife.
There in the van he fought thro' many a dawn,
Stood by the forlorn hope, knew victory ;
Proud, scorning Death, fought with a purpose drawn
Sword-edged, defiant, grand, for Liberty.
He fell : but yielded not his English soul—
That lives out there beneath the battle's roll.

A SOLDIERS' CEMETERY

Behind that long and lonely trenched line
To which men come and go, where brave men die,
There is a yet unmarked and unknown shrine,
A broken plot, a soldiers' cemetery.
There lie the flower of youth, the men who scorn'd
To live (so died) when languished Liberty :
Across their graves flowerless and unadorned
Still scream the shells of each artillery.
When war shall cease : this lonely unknown spot
Of many a pilgrimage will be the end,
And flowers will shine in this now barren plot
And fame upon it through the years descend :
But many a heart upon each simple cross
Will hang the grief, the memory of its loss.

A LARK ABOVE THE TRENCHES

Hushed is the shriek of hurtling shells : and hark !
Somewhere within that bit of deep blue sky,
Grand in his loneliness, his ecstasy,
His lyric wild and free, carols a lark.
I in the trench, he lost in heaven afar ;
I dream of love, its ecstasy he sings ;
Both lure my soul to love till, like a star,
It flashes into life : O tireless wings
That beat love's message into melody—
A song that touches in this place remote
Gladness supreme in its undying note,
And stirs to life the soul of memory—
'Tis strange that while you're beating into life
Men here below are plunged in sanguine strife.

THE WAYSIDE CROSS[1]

Beneath a hawthorn bush, dying, he lay
Upon an orchard slope, a gentle hill ;
The silvery moonlight through the night did play
Upon his blood-stained form silent and still.
The gentle breezes of the night did fan
The perfumes of the spring-time all around ;
Through the night a nightingale did scan
His amorous song in tireless, ceaseless round.
Prostrate he lay upon a mossy bed—
The stars of night watching above his head.

[1] Written under fire and unrevised.—[ED.]

Made in the Trenches

That morning through the village there had tramped
His regiment with a joyous mocking lilt,
Marching unto the line, their faces stamp'd
With purpose, bodies wiry, sinewy built.
Through the ruined shatter'd village he
With comrades brave that morn had passed and gone,
Nor thought to there return for sanctuary
Tired and wounded when the day was done.
Within the maze of the entrenchments he
Scarce had set a foot ere a shell did place
Him on the list of casualties, then he
Returned into the first-aid ambulance base.
Since he could walk ('twas but a wounded arm)
He tramped back with a comrade, going well
Until at sundown near the village farm
He met his fate (his comrade too)—a shell.
His pal was dead, no succour was there nigh.
The sunset died, the moon rose in the sky ;
He crawled unto the bank beneath the thorn
And lay beneath the night, dying—forlorn.

From out the bourne whose outer marge is Death
His spirit waver'd, plumed its broken wings,
Tried to renew beneath each gasping breath
Its vigour at Life's quickly dying springs.
His throat was parched, his body throbbed with pain,
He fought the wave of sleep that numbed his brain ;
He cried for water, help—none were to bless,
To soothe his pain, delirious consciousness.
Sudden his body seemed to lose the throb
Of pain, his spirit fought the shadows vast
That seemed to cloud his memory and rob
Him of the life, the glory of the past.
The moon still shone ; the wind so tenderly
Whisper'd the tale of night's serenity.
A light rushed to his sense, a shadow leapt
Athwart his brain, his vision cleared, across
The pool where wandering moonbeams fell and slept
He saw the silhouette of a wayside cross.

Was it a devil, nightmare that stood there?
Was he on earth or in some haunt of hell?
Ah no! perfumes of flowers were on the air—
Surely he lay in some sweet English dell
Where love-birds sang, where bluebells rang their tune,
Where roses flamed upon the banks of June?
Or in some meadow with sweet violets nigh,
With wild larks trilling love-songs in the sky?
His vision cleared . . . that figure was the Christ,
The Man who died for men, the God who came
And kept on Calvary a woeful tryst
To save humanity from guilt and shame!

He swept across the gulf: he was a child
Kneeling at mother's knee, chanting a prayer
Unto a God, a Saviour meek and mild,
A God whose effigy was hung up there.
Then in that hour he lived again the past—
Its childhood, youth, its vision and its loss,
Its love, its grief, its hope, illusions vast,
The meaning of the suffering of the Cross.
He scampered down the dell, gathered the flowers,
A child enchanted with the sunny hours;
Sought out the wild-bird in the leafy thorn,
Sought out the wonder in the world just born.
He trod its paths flushed with his youthful dreams,
Mad with the urge of love, of high desire,
Cherish'd his visions by the woodland streams
And flung abroad his chansons wing'd with fire.
He felt the touch of hair upon his face;
He heard a voice whose softest tones were bliss;
He felt the joy, the mastery of his race,
When he had won that burning, deathless kiss.
Then pain, then loss, the falsity of friend,
The crush of life, its herculean strife,
Monotony out-wearing, without end,
That which we love, we hate, mysterious—Life!

Made in the Trenches

And then he read the Cross, saw in that dark
Black silhouette against the waning moon,
The symbol of man's greatness ; the quick spark
That lights man onward through the raven gloom.
He felt the pain, the agony of the Christ
Within the shadows of Gethsemane ;
He felt the pain, the glory of that tryst
Kept long ago out there at Calvary.
And with that vision grand at morn he passed—
That he with others yielded up his life
For love of race, Truth's victory at last,
To win a wider vision from the strife ;
The " greater love " that more no man can give,
The sacrifice outpoured that men may live ;
The crown of thorns worn proudly just like He
Who went before—showed men their Calvary.
The thought thrilled through his brain and warmed his
     heart :
He gave one shudder, momently did start,
And then met proudly Death in that lone tryst,
Murmuring as he died : Mother ! England ! Christ !

The moon did wane, dawn stole above the hill,
The lark in heaven poured forth his ecstasy :
The orchards bloom'd, the winds were hushed and still,
And there amid the morn's serenity,
Firm-lipp'd and proud, with victory on his face,
A soldier lay ; " he died for love of race."

CORPORAL JOHN WILLIAM STREETS,
12th Service Battalion,
York & Lancs.,
B.E.F., France.

LIFE ON AN ARMOURED TRAIN

I N a small and unobtrusive railway siding there lies, awaiting the German invader, an iron monster. It pants day and night to get at him, so that the shed is full of smoke; its big guns bristle with eagerness for the fray. At all hours of the day there is a coming and going of men in khaki—a mixed but merry crew. There can be seen the "cheesecutter" of the R.G.A. man, the glengarry of the Royal Scot, and the blue field-service cap of Kitchener's Army.

On board an armoured train one does not lose touch with the verb "to hustle," although the life is not so strenuous as with battalion or battery. Bugle-calls are unheard (which is a blessing). The daily routine is varied and interesting.

One wakens about 7 a.m. to the tuneful call of the cook—

"Any one for coffee, boys? Come away, my lucky didos,—the old firm."

Half awake, one blinks and splutters through a cup of piping coffee. Through the steam can be discerned dim bundles of blankets slowly twisting about, till first a head and then a hand and cup detaches itself. Every one is sitting up. Sounds of

sipping and sighs of satisfaction fill the air. A spirit of restful-
ness follows, for it is essential to snatch forty more winks before
being compelled to " show a leg " by the corporal in charge.

Blanket folding, a dash along the platform, and a wash in a
pailful of hot water from the boiler, are the items which must
be gone through before the whistle sounds for parade. The
O.C. believes in Swedish drill or a route march as an appetizer
for " brekker."

There is nothing artificial about an armoured-train breakfast—no swagger French names attached to it—just plain eggs
and bacon, sausages or " Scotch mist." The cook knows exactly

how to get the best out of his material,
judging by the rows of smiling faces as
the crew march past in single file, each
one, waiter fashion, supporting his plate and
mug. Breakfast over, one responds to the
cry of " Turn out for spuds ! " and slices
and stabs vigorously at a potful of potatoes
and vegetables, at the same time adding
one's quota to whatever popular chorus
happens to be in full swing.

The morning parade is split up into
three parts. Part one consists of a crusade
against dirt and dust. Every speck and smut
must be chased out by broom and scrubber : the fireplace must
be poked at viciously, ashes removed, and so many grains of dust
and soot inhaled : coals have to be fetched up to the cook-house :
gas generators have to be emptied, hosed down, and refilled.

In part two, the platform rings to the brisk tread of the
gunners, resounds to the thud of dummy ammunition, and the
rafters re-echo the sharp words of command as the intricacies of
gun drill are gone through.

Mechanism completes the third part of the parade. Occasionally the morning's work is agreeably varied by a visit to the
swimming baths or shooting range.

After morning parade there is a short and delightful period
of off duty. The crew rallies round the furnace at the far end
of the shed. Scotland, England, Ireland, and Wales are repre-

sented, so it is only natural that the long-suffering rafters have to re-echo boisterous bursts of laughter, until the cook interrupts with the shout, "Dinner up!" The group disperses with a rush, and once again there is a procession of smiling faces and steaming plates, this time replete with steak or stew, potatoes and vegetables, swimming in gravy.

For the afternoon parade much healthy physical and mental benefit is derived from semaphore, or a lightning change act on the cinder track outside. One is made to grasp one's rifle at the slope and then to change it with bewildering rapidity from one position to another, varied by a sort of round game entitled, "On the left at the halt, form squad!" which is apt to be somewhat confusing

to the beginner. The fierce joys of football are sometimes tasted as a pleasant variation. Lusty tussles, well worthy of a Roman amphitheatre, take place between the "Jocks" (aided and abetted by the officers) and the R.G.A.'s.

Preparation for action concludes the business of the day. Each man dashes to his alarm post. Guns are overhauled, stores minutely inspected, portholes opened, ammunition examined, water-supply peered at, fingers checked, and everything made shipshape. When that is properly done the dismissal ceremony takes place. One is then free to frisk about as one pleases, or if on pass (which on the train is a rare occasion) to look out one's walking-out apparel.

Made in the Trenches

In the long winter evenings an atmosphere of peace and tranquillity broods over the train, except when knightly figures, helmeted and wrapped up in bayonet-fighting gear, step forth.

Then do the cinders fly on the cinder track, and bayonet thuds on jacket pad like claps of thunder. Inside the train happy groups crowd round the stove enveloped in clouds of tobacco smoke ; others with tongues lolling forth vibrate the table in prodigious epistolary efforts ; while the quartette in the far corner, one pair smiling broadly and the other gazing gloomily at their fingers, are sure to be indulging in some sort of card game. This goes on till it is time for beds to be made down. The table, the space beneath it, the floor, and all odd corners are laid out with blankets and bedding.

One falls asleep at 10.15 to the soothing lullaby of the sentry's tramp, tramp, along the platform—thanking goodness that it is still an hour or two before it is time to be turned out to take his place.

PTE. R. DRYSDALE SMITH,
5TH R.S., ARMOURED TRAIN.
(From *The Searchlight*.)

THE GARDEN OF SLEEP

ONCE we knew it as "No Man's Land," but now we call it "The Garden of Sleep." Winter gave it the first name and summer the latter, and each in its season was true and appropriate.

A novice in war, I saw it first on a winter's day : one of those dread November afternoons that seem now almost like a bad dream—a grey lowering sky, a damp, penetrating cold, a never-ending, bone-wetting drizzle, and everywhere mud, mud, mud. Mud ! Even the very word looks ugly in print, and, oh God, how we hated the very sound of it ! Was there, we wondered, anything left in the world but mud ? Was the world being overwhelmed by an onflowing tide of mud ? Had we ever known an existence free from it ?

Mad questions perhaps, but there were times when men of strong brains asked themselves such things in all seriousness. We lived like rats in mud, and rats alone lived with us. All other decent animals would have scorned an existence under such conditions, and it was left for the highest and the lowest of the animal race to dwell together.

"No Man's Land" in those days was the culminating point in a walk through the Land of Desolation, the journey's end in a pilgrimage through the Land of Man's Savagery. One started behind the line, where the occupations of life went on much as usual, where the small remnant of the agricultural population still laboured and tilled, where the untrodden grass was still Nature's fair carpet, and where the smell of the earth was not profaned by death and corruption, but was still the sweet breath of Mother Nature.

· · · · · ·

Then as one journeyed up " the Road"—the road of life and death indeed—one could not but note the gradual transition from beauty to ugliness, from life to desolation. Deserted bivouacs, the foul and trampled ground, the littered paper and tins, the dumps of used ammunition, the broken-down transport, a dead horse announcing its presence strongly to the world, closely packed moving bodies of wet and perspiring humanity, while every moment Nature, vanquished in the struggle, gave way more and more to the wave of desolation.

It was a strange thought, but we were spreading over the country like a blight, an army of destruction, as every army must be, and yet an army of salvation and deliverance. After all, are we not illustrating the Psalmist's words that " Out of evil good may come " ?

And now we have come to the area where the reserve trenches sear the land like a long gaping wound, while ahead of us the country-side is scarred and shell-pocked and stripped of vegetation as though swept by an all-devouring fire. It is here that we dive into the communication trench, and passing through these lanes of mud, stepping sometimes on one side to allow the passage to the rear of some reddened clay that only a few minutes ago was a human form, we come at length to the front-line trench and the last stage of our journey.

.   .   .   .   .

Beyond us lies " No Man's Land," a land that cannot even be looked at without risk, except through the medium of a periscope, a land of little intrinsic value, but more carefully guarded than any other piece of land on earth, the sole barrier between two bitterly contending armies, the land of death and deathless bravery. Such is " No Man's Land."

It has its inhabitants, this debatable land, still inhabitants, who lie undisturbed by the swift messengers of death that fly over its surface at all moments of the day and night, inhabitants whose fate has drawn them from all corners of the earth to become joint inheritors in this land of death.

That dark mass in front was once men, cut down like over-ripe corn when victory was almost within their grasp ; gone in one moment from vigorous life to await earth's last great roll-call before the All-seeing and All-pitying. Nature is kind, and the rank grass is doing its best to conceal the hideousness of the pile. Friend and foe together they rest undisturbed; to cross that narrow tract is death, and Death guards Death with jealous care.

It is the altar whereon are offered the sacrifices to the empire lust of a madman, and around lie the votive offerings in the shape of broken weapons of destruction and the silent dead. It is a cruel, hated land, but when we think of all that it has witnessed, deep down in our hearts we know that it is also to us for evermore a sacred land.

.   .   .   .

Summer, gentle and kindly, has been good to us who live and have our being on its outskirts. Under her gentle touch a transformation has taken place, and over this strip of death and decay she has thrown a mantle of waving green grass luxuriantly dotted with the vivid scarlet of the poppy. Indeed, so plentiful are these flowers that what was once called " No Man's Land " is now known to us as " The Garden of Sleep."

It is a lovely name this " Garden of Sleep," and had the whole world been searched no more appropriate one could have been found. It is the garden of sleep of heroes, the Valhalla of the bravest of the brave, Nature's cemetery of the vanguard. It is no longer the culmination of desolation, but an untrodden belt of beauty between two broad tracts of man-defiled country; a belt where Nature, without restraint or restriction, reigns supreme.

In our simple childish way, we carry flowers that fade in a day to the last resting-place of those we love; here, where we are powerless to do it, Nature, with lavish hand and without distinction of class or rank, gives to all a glorious canopy of real living bloom.

.   .   .   .

Perhaps there is something sinister in this luxuriant growth; perchance the blood that has soaked the ground gives to the flower its deep, rich colouring. Who can say? Who will dare to say? Sufficient that it stands a living wreath to the fallen, a living token of how the power of nature can triumph even over the defiling touch of man.

Or, perhaps—and you may call the idea extravagant if you will—there is something higher to us who view it typified in this gorgeous colouring. May it not be, we ask ourselves, that in its bold and almost aggressive beauty it is symbolic of the buoyant life of our nation, that its almost blood-red colour typifies that young manhood that with eagerness has poured, is pouring, and will continue to pour out to take its part in the world war?

The rich red colouring of the flower, the rich warm red blood of English youth, the bold upstanding bloom that shrinks not from the world, the men of our race ever upholding the cause of justice and right. Such is the parallel, extravagant if you like, which occurs to me as I gaze, but it is one on which I love to linger.

LIEUT.-COL. ATKINSON, A.S.C.

WORDY ECONOMY

Being a Totally Imaginary Correspondence Concerning a True Incident

(1)

From Lieut. Dash, " E " Co.,
     99th Bearknease Regiment.

To O/C " E " Co.

     I attach state't of evid'ce regard'g feat of C.S.M. Blank in captur'g enemy sniper s'ngle hand'd on 30th Feb. 16. He espied sniper conceal'd behind house, and, throw'g away rifle and equip't, chased him at full speed. Event'ly brought Germ'n down with stick, but in so doing C.S.M. Blank rec'd 3 wounds, and is today be'g inval'd'd home.

2.3.16.
                                                        Lieut.

(2)

Adj't, 99th Barenees Regt.
     Send you attached.

2.3.16.
                                                        Capt.

(3)

Col., 99th Baerkniese Regt.

Related this to you last night in dug-out just before "minne-werfers" arr'd.

[signature]

2.3.16.   Adj't.

(4)

Bg. Gl., 999th Brig.

For yr cons'd'n.

[signature]

3.3.16.   Col.

(5)

Col., 99 Barneas Regt.

Not my pigeon.   Have no jurisdic'n.

[signature]

4.3.16.   Bg. Gen'l.

(Note.—Ph'nd ap'l'gy.   Rep'd " Cinfairiang," or some'g sim'r.)

(6)

D.A.D.A.B.C.

Encl's'd forw'd with rec'm'd't'n for Mil'y medal.

[signature]

5.3.16.   Col.,
                                                99th Bearkneys Reg't.

Wordy Economy

(7)

D.A.A.B.C.

What do y' think of this? Is it not typ'l as show'g the mater'l and brac'g eff't of expos'g knees to zeph'rs of " la belle France " ?

[signature]

D.A.D.A.B.C.

5.3.16.

(8)

D.A.B.C.

Sugg'st all tr'ps be supp'd with k'lts. Idea's good, n'est c-pas ?

[signature]

D.A.A.B.C.

6.3.16.

(9)

A.B.C.

Agree with foreg'g. Idea means sav'g of time, stat'y, rations, amm'n, h's's, off'rs, and men.

[signature]

D.A.B.C.

6.3.16.

(10)

A.D.C. D.E.F.

Extrem'y amus'd at 1st chap'r of this nov'l.

[signature]

A.B.C.

6.3.16.

(11)

A.B.C.

Agree. High'y del'ght'l. Mais what is y'r recom'n? Didst oubliez?

7.3.16.   A.D.C. D.E.F.

(12)

A.D.C. D.E.F.

Oui. Recom'n afor'men'd w'd app'r best proced'e.

7.3.16.   A.B.C.

(13)

D.E.F.

Att'd w'd app'r worth some'g, don't y' think?

8.3.16.   A.D.C. D.E.F.

(14)

To Ld. Southbank,
    Mt. Carmel Lighthouse, E.C.

DEAR ALF,

        Regard'g encl'd evid'ce. Recomm'd for y'r consid'n C.S.M. Blank be award'd Mil'y medal. Will you cons'r its possibil'y and advis'y.

Yours loving'y,

9.3.16.   D.E.F.,
                                                        British Army, France.

Wordy Economy

(15)

To the D.E.F.,
     British Army, France.

SIR,
     Having consulted my sub-editresses, amuensis, and office girls (there is a war on, you know, and my staff's a female one), I find they agree with myself that the granting of the suggested medal to the C.S.M. mentioned should, without the slightest doubt, be given consideration.
     Yours faithfully,

     P.S.—Cheer up ; with my help, we'll win.   Have you seen today's issue of 12 pages ?

(16)

A.B.C.
     Delight'l, is it not?   Have y' heard any'g about this war he ment'ns ?

14.3.16.   D.E.F.

(17)

D.E.F.
     Yes, I've heard rum'rs.   Shall I make enquiries about it ?

14.3.16.   A.B.C.

(18)

A.B.C.

Don't waste stat'ery.   Have y' no foibles?   Regardez toujours le ne plus ultra de patriotisme, et "carry on."   Compre?

15.3.16.   D.E.F.

(19)

D.A.B.C.

You or the D.A.D. can translate.

15.3.16.   A.B.C.

(20)

D.A.A.B.C.

You are the Frenchman.   I've only been o'seas 11 m'ths.

16.3.16.   D.A.B.C.

(21)

D.A.D.A.B.C.

Can you trace origin'l subj't?

17.3.16.   D.A.A.B.C.

(22)

Col., 99th Bareneasie Regt.
     To note.

[signature]

18.3.16.
                                D.A.D.A.B.C.

(23)

O/C " E " Co.
     For information.

[signature]

19.3.16.
                                      Col.

Lieut. Dash,
     " E " Co.
          For necessary action.

(24)

[signature]

19.3.16.
                                    Capt.

(25)
                         Somewhere in France,
                              20.3.16.

C.S.M. Blank,
         99th Barnies Regt.,
                 Military Hospital, S.W.

Dr. Blank,
     You will notice from the Press (i.e. London Male and Liefe)
that for your courageous action in connection with a certain sniper, you
received the Military Medal. Congrats! Hope you are having a nice
time in " blighty."
                          Yours truly,

[signature]

             S. H. Doddrell, Sergt., R.E.

TUBBY

Tubby ain't no bloomin' angel,
Bless you, sir, I know 'e ain't;
An' I don't suppose 'e'd like it
If you said 'e was a saint.
But 'e's British, is ole Tubby,
Mide of British beef and beer,
An' I bet 'e thinks in 'Ev'n
Ov 'is pals wots left dahn 'ere.
'E was killed last week, was Tubby,
Knocked out sudden-like and flat.
Lord, 'e was a champion bomber,
There ain't any doubt on that!
Them there 'Uns, Gawd 'elp their fices,
Blew up sich a whoppin' mine,
An' our chaps 'opped in the crater,
Lumme, but they 'opped it fine.
Tubby went along wiv others,
Threw 'is bombs and never missed;
When 'e'd thrown 'em all 'e 'ollered,
Cussed 'em like, and shook 'is fist.
Back 'e 'ops wiv shells all rahnd 'im,
Bet you Tubby didn't care,
Says 'e wants more bombs and sich-like,
An' 'e gets 'em then and there.
Back 'e goes, we cheered 'im 'oarsely,
Tubby seemed to think it fun,
Lumme, it was fine to watch 'im
Snap 'is fingers at the 'Un.
But 'e didn't get much farver,
Dropped 'is bombs 'e did, and then,
Then we 'eard 'im shout 'is loudest,

Tubby

" Boys, I'm done," 'e shouts, " an' w'en—
" W'en you writes 'ome to the missus
" Tell 'er Tubby went 'ome game."
An' 'e died like that, did Tubby,
Shoutin' out 'is missus' name.

.   .   .

Yus, I bet, 'e thinks in 'Ev'n
Ov 'is pals wots left dahn 'ere.
Good ole Tubby, 'ow we loved yer,
We shan't fail yer, never fear.

R. F. C.

(From *The Gasper*.)

An Ambulance Convoy.

THE "SURE-TO-BE-HIT" FEELING

Poppy red! Poppy red!
Dusky, vivid, 'mong the dead,
In the trench that is my bed,
Poppy red!

THE doggerel tumbled into my head the other day. I had put down the plank that I was carrying up to the front line. I sat down on a fire-step in a reserve trench and looked up, and there they were on the parapet above my head, leaning over in the breeze, glowing in the bright green grass that rimmed the parapet; poppies, blood-red, swarthy, virile, the same poppies that you have in your fields at home. It was funny. They seemed to suggest that war, after all, is only passing, trivial. What do poppies care for guns and bayonets and dead men? What does nature care? Soon men would be sensible again, and plough the land instead of making ditches in it and holes; soon the madness would pass and nature, that has taken no notice of war, would not even sigh. Soon——

But the plank! So we went on again. But I thought a lot about the poppy. It was sweet and good to look at. So was the sky, cloudless blue with white balls of shrapnel playing like thistle-down in the wind round one or two aeroplanes; so was the singing of birds; so were the trees in full, glorious leaf; so was the old grey stone church, poking its head out among them, mildly inquisitive. They were all very good. They helped one to be cheerful.

Weather plays its part in the winning of this war. The men on both sides of that barbed, ugly, shell-holed strip that nobody owns have a longing for peace in their hearts at moments like that. They can't help it. After all, life is very, very sweet, and even in trenches on summer days, when there's peace for an hour or so, life is good to live. Men are good-natured ; everything is momentarily roseate. A sun-bath in a trench is like a sun-bath anywhere else—if you can forget the war for a minute or two ; and most of us can do that. Most of us are young enough, you see.

On summer days we invent ways of making warfare tolerable, and we gossip. We have begun to love scandal and to live on rumours.

" I think," says one gravely, " both sides ought to club up and shove arc-lamps up between the front lines. Consider the awful waste of all those ' Verey ' lights that are sent up. They're pretty, of course, but if they're for beauty why not more red and green ones, and what's wrong with purples ? What about a competition every night for the best display ? But I do think arc-lamps are the thing. Imagine Piccadilly lit by ' Verey ' lights ! They're out of date."

" Music is what I miss," says another. " There's too little variety in the noises. It's always a crash, a bang, a whistle, a wail, or a hiss. Now my idea is that each shell should have attached to it a gramophone record and needle, and as the shell revolves hurtling through the air, the music would amuse and entertain vastly—to say nothing of holding the enemy so entranced that he would never seek to escape the thing. One can easily suggest appropriate songs. What of ' I'm Longing For My Ain Folk ' ; ' You Made Me Love You ' ? You could have a salvo playing ' See Them Shuffling Along,' and a whiz-bang might give ' Hitchy-koo ' instead of its infernal bang-bang. On a clear night you could work off your spare 9·2's in couples on ' The Moon Hath Raised Her Lamp Above.' And in a big bombardment I don't see why we shouldn't charm them with Wagner's ' Meister-singers.' There's not enough originality about the ordnance people."

Made in the Trenches

After these brilliant young gentlemen have thus unburdened themselves there are the jokes to be grimly perpetrated, as follows :—

"Owen's in for it."
"Which Owen ?"
"Hohenzollern !"
And :—
"Heard about Auchy ?"
"What Auchy ?"
"Bumps !"
(We leave a man out of trenches specially to think them out.)

. . . . .

Lastly, the latest tales are told. Luckily the other day we had some new troops in with us for instruction, and new troops do funny things. First of all I had better point out that a whiz-bang is a small 12-pounder shell fired at short range at incredible speed. It derives its name from the fact that the noise it makes is a whiz, followed at once by the report of the burst. It is utterly impossible to see them. Now a trench mortar is hurled high in the air, comes slowly, and can be easily seen. Sentries are posted to watch for them in the sky and to blow warning whistles of their approach that people may dodge them.

One of our officers went along to a new sentry—not a mortar sentry—staring fixedly in his periscope.

Officer : "What are your duties ?"

Sentry : "To watch in this 'ere glass for whiz-bangs."

That was funny enough, but farther along was the mortar sentry blowing his whistle to warn people of whiz-bangs that, of course, had burst already.

Whiz-bang ! Then a shrill blast.

"What was that ?" asked the officer.

"Trench mortar, sir," was the calmly confident reply.

"Did you see it ?"

"Yes, sir."

Whiz-bang ! again. Another blast.

"Did you see that too?"

"Yes, sir; seen 'em all."

"My lad," said the officer, "you're a marvel."

.   .   .   .   .

Unfortunately it isn't always sunny. Neither are we. Weather plays its part; but whether or not you are cheerful out here depends mainly on spirit. It is mostly all a matter of spirit, or, as a Lancashire man would say, of "guts." Without spirit life would be intolerable. You simply must keep a hold over yourself, not thinking too much of the pleasures and the dear ones at home or the risks you run here.

.   .   .   .   .

I suppose that very many of us here have had periods when we were convinced that we were going to be hit. My own experience is that they last half a day, or maybe as long as two or three. You start, perhaps, by going on duty two or three times in succession, just as the gentle Hun has a fit of industry and shells you; or two nights in succession you work on the parapet; or the day when you are to be relieved is postponed. Sometimes a very vivid dream that you are being killed will do it, or maybe a letter from some one at home saying they are convinced they will never see you again. This "sure-to-be-hit" sensation is mighty unpleasant. You notice everything that seems to be added proof, and everything you do seems to make death doubly certain. You are sent on a message to some part of the line that receives more than its fair share of minenwerfers, or, if you are a mess orderly, you are suddenly transferred to some other duty and kept in the trenches all day, or if you are in billets you are sent up to the front line on a working party.

One is particularly susceptible to the feeling just before going home on furlough. If the news that one is for leave comes in the trenches, most of us, I imagine, are certain that we shall be killed before we get out of them. One remembers tales of men out here for eighteen months and then killed as they walked out to go to "Blighty"; or a 'bus-load of them caught by a shell as they went down the road.

The "sure-to-be-hit" periods are rare (I can remember two in seven months). It is well that they are. Being "off colour" is accountable for some of them, and the losing temporarily of one's grip over oneself for the remainder. It would be easy to be miserable and depressed. Cheeriness is mainly a matter of spirit.

PTE. J. HODSON.
(From *The Daily Mail*.)

MAKING IT CLEAR

Should you be in a restaurant one of these days—
You called in, say, just for a wet—
And if at a table you happened to see
Two men in a lather of sweat
(Brown and Jones, say, their names) ; they are waving
    their arms
And shouting. It's easy to guess
That if you're attentive and don't mind the row,
You'll overhear something like this :—

" When Hindenburg's army was rushed to the East,
It was said that the Russians would mizzle ;
To answer his critics, the Russian Grand Duke
Began to invest Przemsyl.
He also prepared to begin his great march
Across the Carpathian passes,
Where he caused the bold Austrian army to run
Like a lot of Pygmalion asses."

Made in the Trenches

Thus Brown. "If you'll hand me the cruet," said Jones,
"With its aid I'll endeavour to show
How Hindenburg's legions were kept on the move,
And how Nicky invested Cracow.
Put the salt-cellar there : that'll represent Lodz,
The downfall of which we foresaw ;
And now if you'll hand me that bottle of beer,
We'll just put it here : that's Warsaw.

Now Hindenburg's plan was to hack his way through,
And Lodz to bombard with his Krupp ;
But he grumbled at last when he entered the town
That Nicky had sold him a pup.
He had fallen right back on the line Zaklakchine "
(" Have a swig at Warsaw, it'll ease yer,"
Said Brown), " and the artful old blighter had gone
And abandoned his grip on Silesia.

If Nicky had stuck in the salt-cellar there
He'd have got a tin hat, nothing's surer ;
For Hindenburg's army, attacking his flank,
Would advance from the line of the Bzura.
But Nicky was wise, and withdrew all his troops
And entrained 'em, with most of their kits,
For the line Krasno-Jaslov-Inowlodz-Dakla-Pass,
With his base at the town Zverzinits."

186

Making it Clear

"Half a moment," quoth Brown, "not a minute ago
You said that the Russians had been
And withdrawn on a totally different line,
So it's evident what you have seen
In the papers has addled your brain, nothing less ;
And if you'll dry up for a spell,
Exactly I'll show how the Russian Grand Duke
Hoped to sign Hindy's passport to Hell.

That mustard-pot there is the Vistula's banks,
And the bread is the Dukla Pass ;
Now look what you've done ! you've been and upset
The remainder of Warsaw, you ass.
Never mind, the bottle will do for that town,
And the beer the Masurian Lakes ;
The sauce-boat's Pilitza. Now, if you don't mind,
Just hand me that basket of cakes.

Put the creamy one there, that'll do for Jukoff,
While the others, spread out in a line,
Represent Sochaczlw, Bolimoff, Wislica,
Pinczow, and Nijnitarezine."

Made in the Trenches

"That's done me," said Jones ; "no more I'll attempt
To argue ; my reason it quails ;
I can only remark, it's a ruddy good job
That our Western front isn't in Wales."

N. RAMSAY,
S.S., R.E., Downing Point.
(From *The Searchlight*.)

HINTS FOR WAR BRIDES

1. *Obtaining a War Husband.*

TAKE one large soldier—preferably Canadian or Australian, as they are much more tractable—smile sweetly until he blushes with confusion, then seize him by the left elbow and guide him gently but firmly home to tea. Gag him with a piece of mother's home-made cake, and whilst he is struggling with that obtain the help of your young brothers and old-maid sisters and tie him securely to a chair (mother's apron-strings will be found useful for this).

Standing in front of the now helpless victim, make a swift passing of the hands, at the same time fixing him with a baleful left eye and repeat slowly, and in even tone, the magic formula "He loves me, he loves me not," until the victim passes away into a state of hypnotic coma. Procure a minister and have him read over the Marriage Service until he gets to the passage "Wilt thou have this, etc.?" It is advisable to pause a while here and wait until the victim recovers. As soon as he opens his eyes papa will whisper in his ear, "Will you have a drink?" and on the victim eagerly exclaiming "I will!" the minister will continue the service. After untying him the rest of the family will retire from the parlour and you spend the rest of a blissful evening explaining how much cheaper you can furnish a house at the "Midland."

2. *Discipline.*

(*a*) After obtaining a war husband, do not allow him to go out for the first week without an escort, as some have been known to be in such a bewildered state during this time that they have forgotten their home address and have been unable to return.

Made in the Trenches

(*b*) Always insist that he gets up at " Reveille," lights the fire and cooks the breakfast—it keeps him in training for the trenches —and, incidentally, enables you to have that extra hour's snooze you always longed for.

(*c*) Make him attend to your orders " without hesitation or remark." He will get into the habit of doing this, eventually, if he values peace and quietness, but it is just as well to start him right.

(*d*) See that he always " salutes" properly, but don't let him practise on your " flapper" sister—" it ain't wise."

(*e*) Practice squad drill " with intervals," and " skirmishing" frequently—he likes it all the better when you " close up" to him.

(*f*) Don't mind him being all " attention" when you have girl friend visitors ; but don't allow him to " present arms."

(*g*) Give him a short " working party " each morning ; he'll appreciate it—maybe.

(*h*) Allow him to smoke in moderation ; but if you want to live the day out don't let him light an " 'Arf a Mo" or a " Kitchener " cigarette.

(*i*) Open warfare should be avoided except " enveloping tactics and encircling movements."

(*j*) Don't " parade" him unnecessarily—it isn't done in the best of circles—really.

(*k*) Don't place all " Estaminets out of bounds" to him— he's only human.

3. *Rations.*

" Bread and cheese and kisses" are usually considered sufficient for the first week by civilians, but owing to the generous issue of cheese in the army, it is better to cut out this item and give a double issue of kisses.

4. *Rum Issue.*

This should be handled with greatest care—a half issue should be sufficient for the first week, as he will naturally be in a high state of mental exhilaration—a double issue should always be given when your mother is going to visit you, when you are

190

going to demand money for a new hat, or at any other such critical times.

5. *Passes.*

Permanent all-night passes should be stopped immediately you have secured him. Short passes for the purpose of visiting " Picture shows," the National Portrait Gallery, or the Zoo may be granted sparingly—Saturday afternoon passes to the River at Richmond or Hendon should be firmly refused.

6. *Pay.*

This demands most careful attention—a mutual banking account is usually found to be the easiest way, with an equal division of work and responsibility. In the majority of families this desirable arrangement is obtained by the husband depositing the money and the wife drawing it out. Needless to add, this simple system of financing the home has been most deservedly popular—with the wives.

7. *General.*

If you find the experiment is not a success, don't fly to divorce. It is much easier, these times, to explain to him how you would just love to read of him having captured a trench full of Germans single-handed, and how you will idolize him when he returns with a V.C., and then persuade him to return to France ; and when the casualty list records him " killed in action," try again.

8. Final, and not by any means the least important hint ; take *Punch's* advice to those about to marry, and—" Don't!"

(I know you won't take notice of this last hint, but I had to put it in so that some time in the dim and distant future I can say, " I told you so !")

(From The Listening Post.)

The Spectre.

Shortly before the outbreak of war a young Frenchman, travelling in Belgium, three times dreamed he saw a white dove in the clutch of a large eagle.

" All nature seems to smile, and sweet content
   To find a haunt with peace in this fair land."
So mused the youth, on idle pleasure bent,
   Roaming with foreign tread old Belgia's strand.—
For now from his ethereal vault the sun
   Each pleasing landscape bathed in golden dew,
And gentle winds from shady coverts won
   Ambrosial waves, which served but to embue
The sense with ecstasy and witching charm,
   For list, the thrush's mellow note had kissed
Each wave to speed its airy race, and arm
   The mind of man against the Stoic mist.
Anon, an ancient pile, with towers grey,
   Breathing of mystery and dim romance,
Mayhap would meet the stranger's eye, and stay
   Its roving flight to greet this happy chance.—
And here a tiny hamlet, nestling close
   Under the wing of some thick-bowered steep,

The Spectre

Would seem a home of infinite repose
  Wherein no worldly strife could ever peep.—
At last upon a bank with ivy hung
  And wreathed with flowerets of the softest hues,
The wanderer now himself with ardour flung
  To meditate at length his eager muse.—
Hard by, a shady brook, whose soothing lay
  Long had lurked in Morpheus' drowsy train,
Laughingly pursued its radiant way,
  Dissolving in its wake such sweet refrain
As lulled the hearer's fancy, and with ease
  Drew back the flimsy lattice veiling sleep.
And sleeping came a dream which seemed to seize
  His mind with horror and foreboding deep.—

.   .   .   .   .

High in the flaming sky a tiny cloud,
  A silver oasis in the desert blue,
Long years ago perchance a throne endowed
  Eternal, when from out the heavens there flew
That messenger to mark the Master's state,
  Now on its gleaming crest a Dove revealed.—
Snow-white its plumes, which seemed to radiate
  Such glowing threads as only that could yield
Which first should intercept old Helios' rays.—
  Around a pomp of noble graces turned
(Of late the everlasting theme of praise
  Of those who first, alas! their virtue spurned),
For all were of the essence of that bliss
  Of which on earth their lord the symbol stood.—
O Peace divine! that man should e'er dismiss
  Thy sacred measure from the scale of good!
Undimmed had been the prospect, clear the view,
  While stately calm, with unresisting might,
Around the Bird of Peace her mantle threw,—
  But now upon the farthest verge of light
Abrupt a shadow loomed, of sullen air,
  As when far off some lowering clouds first blot

Made in the Trenches

The virgin blue and bid the sailor 'ware
   The gathering storm, so seemed with evil fraught
This visitation drear.—With motion swift
   It rode the airy main, and soon the flight
Of intervening space served to uplift
   The haze which distance lent, and in the light
Sweet Peace diffused, a hideous form disclosed,
   Sad emblem of calamity and woe,
A Mailéd Fist, upon whose front reposed
   An Eagle of forbidding mien, the glow
Of passion in whose eye seemed to proclaim
   The cult of might the means to every end,
Tyrannic sway the end of every aim—
   False images, that oft on earth attend
Proud princes and the soaring schemes of men.—
   High o'er the Bird of Peace the spectre hung,
While far below, where harmony till then
   Had reigned supreme, uneasiness unsprung,—
For envy now and avarice and hate
   Shot from those baleful eyes as they reviewed
Earth's fairest lands wrapped in that happy state
   Prosperity and peace alone endued.—
At last its brooding glance swept in its train
   The Sentinel of each pacific ray,
And, like a steed freed from the curbing rein,
   Down swooped the dismal fury on its prey
And crushed the slender frame.—Accursed blow!
   The knell of happiness in countless homes,
For with, alas! the sacred Bird laid low,
   Across the world grim War relentless roams,
And in his wake a plague of horror strews
   As ne'er before on earth had wrought such woe.—
And there the dreamer's fancy frighted views,
   O heavy change! the land where to and fro
Caprice of late his wandering steps had bent
   Entranced, a region now of spoil and gloom
Where desolation dwelt, and loud lament
   And sad despair sought refuge in the tomb.—

.   .   .   .

The Spectre

And now the sun had reached his western gate,
    While his late rays, shorn of their fervid might,
No longer with their warmth propitiate
    The cooling breeze, whose gentle touch to flight
Impels soft slumber's minions, and recalls
    Betimes the wanderer from his troubled dream.
A dream no more, alas! for ere night falls
    The Teuton hordes, in never-ending stream,
Surge o'er that land of peace and blithe outlook,
    And blood proclaims the advent of "The Day."—
Blind count! that in the sum no reckoning took
    Of that divine decree, "I will repay!"

GUNNER J. T. HENDERSON,
No. 2 COMPANY, FORTH R.G.A., Downing Point.
(From *The Searchlight*.)

TOLD IN A DUG-OUT

An officer in a well-known infantry regiment recently came home from the Front on short leave. Whilst in "Blighty" he received a letter from a colleague whom he had left in the trenches. The letter ended thus: "I wish the blighters would come and relieve this monotony, we'd chase the whole lot to hell."

The last word had been deleted by the censor, who appended this footnote: "I understand that all references to future movements of troops are strictly forbidden."

.   .   .   .   .

Recently an officer had occasion to stop "one day's pay" of a private for the crime of losing his mess-tin.

"Did you have your name on it?" he inquired.

"Yes, sir, I scratched it on."

"You what !!"

"Scratched it on, sir—with a knife."

"How dare you disfigure Government property! We'll make it two days' pay."

.   .   .   .   .

A strictly moral married man who joined up in a hard-worked infantry regiment, was horrified to find himself the object of the drill sergeant's sanguinary wrath. Feeling deeply the ignominy of being sworn at before the whole company he decided to lodge a complaint with the C.O.

C.O. "You say the sergeant used foul language to you?"

Recruit. "Yes, sir (with a blush), he called me a—er *ruddy* fool."

C.O. (reflectively). "A *ruddy* fool, eh !—and you didn't like it?"

Recruit. "No, sir, I certainly did not."

196

C.O. " And you're not a ruddy fool ? "

Recruit. " No, sir—not a bit."

C.O. " Well, then ; just you go straight to the sergeant and tell him he's a *ruddy* liar."

.   .   .   .   .

A very young junior officer who took part in the immortal landing at Gallipoli wrote home to his mother, giving her a vivid description of his experiences. He concluded : " I must confess, mother dear, that I felt a little funky once we were off the good old ship and afloat in that little boat. Huge shells from the Turkish batteries were hitting the water and exploding all round us, and the machine-gun fire was like the buzzing of a million bees. Boats were being sunk every second, and I really thought the end was nigh. When the din was at its worst I remembered the padre's words, ' When in danger always look to Heaven.' Well, I looked to Heaven, and hang me if there wasn't a blessed aeroplane dropping bombs on us."

.   .   .   .   .

As an instance of the appalling mistakes which telegraphists sometimes make, the following story is an excellent example. A young officer who wrote to his wife daily from France was suddenly given a few days' leave. There was no time to wire from Calais, so he hurried on to the transport and determined to telegraph his home-coming to his wife immediately he reached Dover. He had a dreadful passage, and to make matters worse was compelled by decency to give up his berth to an elderly lady who had just returned from the base hospital, where she had, by special permission, been to visit her badly wounded son. Four hours' later his wife received the following telegram from Dover :—

" Expect home immediately. Dreadful passage, awfully sick. Gave *birth* to old lady on leaving Calais."

G. G.

THE MOANER

(Dedicated to the-(Censor)-, A/Adj. to the 1st Moaners Battalion, and greatest living authority on the subject.)

Did ever you hear of the poor moaning man,
Who's built on the grumbling and all-grousing plan,
Who murmurs strange oaths from each early dawn,
And continues complaining in tones all forlorn?
Till night closes in and slumber prevails,
This poor moaning mortal his fate e'er bewails.

We have such a man in our number eight,
Whose troubles and trials I'll try to relate.
He'd moan at the stars, he'd moan at the moon,
He'd moan at the lasses when out for a spoon.
He'd moan at his breakfast because 'twas hot,
He'd moan at his dinner because it was not;
He'd moan at the sergeants and wish them in H—l
And if they should get there, he'd moan just as well.

He'd moan at the mud and he'd moan at the dust,
He'd moan at his rifle and leave it to rust,
He'd grouse at the Germans and fume at the French,
And mumble his curses on mortar or trench.
He'd moan at the horses, the wagons, the goat,
He'd moan at his harness, his boots or his coat.
But one thing gave rise to no little surprise
When he moaned at the cook-house about the chef's pies.

The Moaner

He'd moan at a private, a sergeant or sub,
He'd moan upon entering a popular pub,
His comrades were stupid, or noisy, or dumb,
He'd moan if they had or had not some rum.
Never, I ween, has this wicked world seen
So morbid a moaner or kicker so keen.
It came to the ears of Headquarters at last,
And a major they made him (promotion is fast),
But he moaned all the more—far worse than before.

So they dubbed him a martyr till after the war,
And gave him the run of the Q.M. Store,
With a team of rare moaners with grievances sore,
A batman or two who had nought else to do
But sit still and grouse at their duties so few;
The pick of the Moaners Battalion were they,
For they mumbled all night and they grumbled all day.
But nobody seemed one penny the worse
Except the poor readers of this wretched verse,
And so when he quits this weary old earth,
Be sure he will haunt us in trouble or mirth.
His shadow will murmur when we tell the tale,
Of how we fought Germans and drank Belgian ale.

G. J. G.,
No. 8 Co., Divl. Train.
(From *The Listening Post.*)

THE PADRE

' Passon 'e do preach a 'mazin' foine zurmon, but 'e be a bit over my head like. Zumtimes I wonders if 'e quite zees things in the zame zort o' way as we do. 'E's terrible hard on a zinner.''

So runs the comment of Farmer Smith to his neighbour, as they slowly make their way down the churchyard path at the close of evensong. It was a scene for an artist, that service from which they had just emerged· The sun is just setting, and through the stained-glass windows of the old Norman church its dying rays fall upon the altar and choir stalls, flooding them with a very riot of colour.

Immaculate in white surplice and crimson stole the vicar is concluding his sermon, an appeal for the mission to Polynesian natives. In measured and cultured tones he begs for that assistance which is so necessary to carry on the work among "the poor benighted heathen," and to bring them from that darkness in which they live into the bright light of religion and civilization —to bring them, in fact, though he does not say so in so many words, into that blissful state of existence in which his congregation are permitted to dwell. To them much has been given, from them much will be expected.

It is all so typically English—the beautiful interior, the reverent and well-dressed congregation, the dignified and well-ordered service, the last dying rays of the sun lighting up the old oak carving, and outside God's Acre, where the branches of the ancient yews wave over the last resting-place of generations of villagers.

The sermon draws to a close with a last forceful appeal, and as the shadows lengthen on the old Norman pillars and the light of day gives way to that of candle and lamp, the notes of the closing hymn peal through the old church. It is the

ideal hymn for the close of an evening service, a hymn of
unutterable beauty and sweetness—

> Swift to its close ebbs out life's little day ;
> Earth's joys grow dim, its glories pass away ;
> Change and decay in all around I see ;
> O Thou, who changest not, abide with me.

.   .   .   .   .

It is late on the Sunday afternoon, and under the shadow
of a few trees about a couple of miles behind the line there lie a
crowd of rough and somewhat dishevelled officers and soldiers,
who have just come out of the trenches and are awaiting the
coming of the padre for a Sunday afternoon voluntary service.

It is a strange setting for a religious service. Around lies
the debris of a bivouac, empty jam tins and biscuit boxes, with
piles of barbed wire, ammunition boxes, entrenching tools, and
all the unpicturesque impedimenta required by trench warfare.
Washing hangs from every tree and bush. A little green dell,
once the playground of the village children, is now occupied
by the horse lines of the regimental transport, and its soft turf
is cut up beyond repair by the passage of many wagons. The
little copse, under which the congregation are waiting, was
once a beauty spot in the countryside, but now it is little
more than a scene of desolation, the destruction for fuel and
by shell fire having gone on side by side. War has taken its
full toll from Nature here.

It is at this moment that the padre rolls up on a bicycle,
no light, easy-running machine, but the old steam-roller Government issue that will stand anything, but requires almost unusual
strength to push it along. " Sorry to be late, sir," he apologizes
to the senior officer present, " but the last lot at X (four miles
away) wanted a couple of extra hymns, and it made me a bit
late. If you're ready now we'll push ahead. I've done four
turns—I mean services—to-day, and I'm booked for another three
yet, and am running a little behind scheduled time."

Sect matters little ; the service is wide enough for all, and
differences of doctrine fade away in the presence of the elemental.

Made in the Trenches

A few short prayers, a lesson, a couple of hymns, and then a five-minute sermon, a manly, modest sermon, that not only braces each one to duty, but carries many a thought back to the home across the Channel. It is almost Kiplingesque in its exhortation to " Go to yer Gawd like a soldier." " You have your duty," so the conclusion runs ; " do it, and God will give you your reward."

The assembly rise from their sitting posture to receive the blessing, and then addressing them the padre says : " Before we sing ' The King ' I expect you fellows would like another hymn. Will some one please choose one ? There is a silence for a moment, and then a most unlikely-looking person—one of the " tough nuts " of the unit, whose very presence at a voluntary service is a source of wonder—suggests " Abide with me."

It is at this moment that the German batteries commence their usual spell of evening hate, and almost punctuating the words of the hymn come the sound of the guns that are carrying mutilation and death to our comrades " up yonder."

> Swift to its close (boom) ebbs out life's little day (boom, boom) ;
> Earth's joys grow dim, its glories pass away (boom) ;
> Change and decay in all around I see (boom) ;
> O Thou, who changest not (boom), abide with me (boom, boom).

.   .   .   .   .

" *The Lord gave, and the Lord hath taken away ; blessed be the Name of the Lord.*"

The well-trained and modulated voice rings clear in the night air, but there is more than a suspicion of a sob in it. The scene is a British cemetery at the Front, and it is the evening following an attack. Here lies part of the harvest of one man's vanity and lust of power, a long, long trench (My God, how long !) in which shoulder to shoulder, even as they charged in that last grand rush, rest those who have fallen. Only a portion of the day's harvest of death, but every one of these silent figures means at least one home plunged into bitter grief and life-long sorrow.

202

The Padre

The service must be hurried; the enemy's artillery have recommenced, the shells are coming nearer and nearer, and any moment may mean annihilation. Look over in that corner; yesterday it was part of the graveyard, with its rows of wooden crosses, and now it is only a hole in which one might easily put a horse and cart.

At any moment the ground on which we stand may be like that, and life must not be unnecessarily sacrificed, even in reverence to the dead. The death-dealing chorus is bursting out with renewed fury, but still the steady voice goes on: *"Therefore, my beloved brethren, be ye stedfast, unmoveable, always abounding in the work of the Lord, forasmuch as ye know that your labour is not in vain in the Lord."*

.   .   .   .   .

"My Gawd, I'm 'it!'"

A gurgling, half-choking cry, and dropping from the platform, 0136 Private William Jones dropped in a crumpled heap at the bottom of the trench. Only a casualty, just one of a large unit, a mere molecule in the great mass, but still somebody's child.

A soiled khaki figure whose Maltese Crosses on his tunic alone tell his vocation, hurries up from where he has just concluded bandaging a wounded man, and gently raises the dying man's head.

"Don't trouble, padre," the words come in fitful gasps. "I'm done in; my number's up. I've been a bad lot, but I tried to do my little bit."

"God knows," and there was a world of pathos in the tone; "and He is more merciful than man."

.   .   .   .   .

The sermon was drawing to an end, as the shadows lengthened in the old parish church.

"And so each man shall be judged according to his lights: from some much shall be expected, from others little, and many who in this world in our limited judgment did poorly, shall at the Great Examination be found to have indeed 'made good.' "

"*And now to God the Father . . . henceforth and for evermore. Amen.*"

There was a rustling of pages as the congregation found the closing hymn, under cover of which Farmer Smith murmurs to his neighbour, "Passon 'e do seem a hundred times more human-like since 'e came back from the war."

Lieut.-Col. Atkinson, A.S.C.

"STANDING BY"

SOLILOQUY OF PRIVATE SELKIRK

I AM weary of all that I wear,
Plain khaki with nought to relieve,
Not to mention my closely cropped hair
And the absence of stripes on my sleeve.
Promotion! O! tell unto me
Thy secret, to others so plain,
Does it rest solely with my O.C.?
If so, I should seek thee in vain.

I am far from my parents and kin,
I must fight out my battles alone,
And until I have conquered Berlin,
Cannot hope to return to my own.
The mice that stroll over my traps
My scowl with indifference see,
Till at length on the verge of collapse,
I "go sick," and put down "M. and D." !

Variety, comfort and peace
Accepted as matters of course—
How I long for the Kaiser's decease,
And the end of this maddest of wars!
Old habits I then might resume
To a length never dreamt of before—
Spend hours in the billiard-room
And never slope hipes any more.

Made in the Trenches

Ye Huns that have caused me this pain,
Discharge at this part of the line
A "single" for Blighty again,
By bullet, trench mortar, or mine.
You certainly now and then send
Some missile that almost—not quite—
Is a means justified by the end :
Why on earth, don't you do it outright ?

How weird is the scream of a shell !
Compared with the noise of its flight,
The street organ suits me quite well
And the howl of a tom-cat at night.
When I think of the days of lang syne
In a moment I seem to be free,
But the mention of saphead or mine
Soon brings back my bondage to me.

But the mouse has returned to her nest,
And the rat is laid down in his lair,
Even here is a season of rest,
And I to my dug-out repair.
There's distraction in every place,
And distraction—encouraging thought—
Can even discomfort efface,
And bring me relief—*of a sort !*

JAP.
(From *The Gasper*.)

THE WINGED HUN

WHEN I write of the enemy with wings, it has nothing to do with the Taube, the Aviatik, and the Fokker.

Only with the fly.

We can and shall beat the Germans; but if the length of our stay in France depended on a success all along the line against the fly we should arrive home in the year 1950 with beards. We should swear. We should emigrate to Greenland—where there are no flies, or ought not to be—and the escape from flies would probably put another twenty-five years on our lives.

Before I left home I heard of hygienists warning Londoners to kill flies. But you don't know what flies are. I didn't.

I had heard a man who had come back from France say, "I would rather do three days in the trenches without flies than one day with them."

I didn't believe him. But now I know that is just because the man at home cannot put himself into the point of view of the soldier abroad.

The New Army man says things which are taken for granted in the Service, but quite startling outside it. And because we have this incongruity in the two views, we have also the explanation why the ideas of the New Army can never be put into print completely.

Strategy on Wings.

When I heard the above-quoted remark I didn't believe it. I hadn't been to France at the time. Now I can appreciate it.

The ordinary fly forms himself into an unconquerable army so far as active service is concerned.

207

He attacks you on your way across ; he waits upon you at your first meal in France ; he buzzes round you from the very moment you place your head upon what does for a pillow ; he attacks and counter-attacks if you try him with smoke, gum-paper, or powder ; he never leaves you, and he refuses to forsake you.

I hope that this will not be taken as an invitation to offer all sorts of remedies to the War Office, which long before I found it all out knew that the fly was one of the enemies and has done its best to minimize the nuisance.

But the fly is a more fertile enemy than the German ; has inexhaustible reserves ; cannot be shot by snipers ; and doesn't care a dash for high explosives.

The fly is the best fighter in creation.

Nothing else on wings or on legs has been known to make itself so comfortable in the war atmosphere.

The fly simply loves a real good strafing ; he revels in a bayonet attack on a warm summer's day. Your first attempt to assail General Fly and his legions was the ordinary treacle-paper business. His strategy was on the Prussian model.

Sufficient numbers were sacrificed to make a carpet for the rest to enjoy the treacle. We next tried gas—a piece of burning paper to smoke out the hundreds which had invaded our tent. The flies lasted longer than the burnt paper. The General had tremendous resources.

Attrition Futile.

Since those first days we have grown hardened. We have decided that the only real way to retaliate upon General Fly is to show indifference—to put up with an attack or two as a sort of inoculation and to take the rest as a matter of course.

A policy of attrition is futile. The armies of the Allies could never "attrite" the armies of General Fly.

He is with us while the summer months and the war last— an uncompromising enemy, an unconquerable foe, tolerable only through a purgatory of restless nights and thousands of bites.

The other day I overheard a group of Tommies discussing the effect of flies upon the military campaign.

One Lancastrian said that when his company went over the

parapet at —— the flies were so thick that they formed a curtain barrier, as good as artillery's, from German machine-guns. This was hardly true, but nearly.

Another asked whether the problem was as acute on the German side.

"Nah," was the Cockney rejoinder; "flies only like good stuff, and they'll keep off Fritz."

The general conclusion, however, was that although Tommy appreciated General Fly's partiality for the armies of the Allies, he probably attacked the enemy as well.

We've got used to these 24-hour attacks of General Fly, and although we can't say that we like them as much as, say, a glass of English beer or a bath now and then, nevertheless we shall miss our little torturers when the hot days are gone. But that is not yet. It is hot weather and the flies are with me as I sign this.

"X."

(From *The Evening News.*)

The " Blues."

TOLD IN A DUG-OUT

A CERTAIN private in a swell infantry regiment was seen going through a series of mysterious rites with rifle and bayonet.

"What do you think you are doing?" he was asked.

"Bayonet exercise," was the indignant reply in cultured tones. "Stabbing people, you know!"

.   .   .   .   .

A wounded soldier in a crowded omnibus rose to give up his seat to a lady.

"No, thank you," she replied. "I should not like to take your seat if you have been wounded!"

"Madam," he answered, "I have been wounded three times, and would be wounded a fourth if you didn't take it."

.   .   .   .   .

The head of the munitions factory was very strict, and, furthermore, was inclined to be a trifle hasty. He had instituted in his shell shop a system of fines for being late, fines for mistakes, fines for spoiled work, and so on. Of course the war rush had made him keener than ever, and, happening to awake one morning very early, he went to the factory a little after starting time. As he got out of his motor-car he saw a pale, haggard, hollow-eyed man walking wearily through the gate.

"Aha, Tom Taylor!" he shouted angrily. "Ten minutes late, eh? Well, you're fined twopence. Not a word, now; that's the rule!"

"Take your time, guv'nor," answered Taylor, "I ain't knocked off from yesterday yet!"

.   .   .   .   .

Somewhere in Flanders a young soldier had been on the sick-list for some time, and now, after a few days' rest, looked very fit for service.

Made in the Trenches

However, he was once more on the sick-list the day his battalion was to leave for the trenches.

"Can you write, my lad?" asked the medical officer.

Suddenly the bright prospect of a nice office job in safety seemed to open before him, so he answered emphatically—

"Yes, sir, I can. I was a clerk in civil life."

"Very well. Now you just write a nice letter to your best girl and tell her you are going to the trenches to-night."

.   .   .   .   .

Young infantryman home from the front on four days' leave, giving a vivid description of a recent strategical retirement :

"It was a wonderful retreat, sir, the most wonderful retreat of the war. We retired without losing a man or a gun——"
(Voice of a crippled warrior from the rear)—"or a moment!"

G. G.

"THE BULL RING"

IF you are infirm or too old to fight you will not be aware that bull-fighting exists in France ; if you have arrived at the "B.E.F." you will know all about it.

Your first few days in France will be spent in the Bull Ring, where grim combat is daily waged between discipline and efficiency and their lack. The matadors are there, also the red cloths. That the Scots instructors are matadors actually is given point by their red-tasselled Balmorals. Their word of command and vigilant eyes are the scarlet cloths. But no ! The red cloth is represented by the blood-dyed uniforms of the fallen, and the *raison d'être* of the Bull Ring is their being brandished before the eyes of the young soldier to train him into that standard cf efficiency which alone can avenge his predecessor in the great fight and enable him to " carry on " in the same fine style.

Junior officers and men are the bulls. The subaltern officer, very nearly bursting with efficiency, and men having done months of bayonet-fighting and practice bombing at home, and who think they know everything short of thrusting a bayonet into a Hun, find their way into the melting-pot, and recent weather has assuredly made of it a veritable melting-pot. In the Bull Ring, apart from receiving instruction in the very latest details used in the firing-line for assailing the enemy and having discipline hurled among them with the force of high explosive, they are subjected to inoculation. " There's only one good German and that's a dead German," is an axiom of a dour Scots instructor.

In itself, getting to the Bull Ring from the particular portion of the extensive camp to which the " bull " belongs will tend to take a certain amount of buck out of him, for the dusty route thereto is something akin to forcing a passage through a vast pepper-pot and Rugger " scrum " combined and being conᴛinually marched at attention withal. There will be many another party besides that to which he belongs wending its way to the sunken, sandy plain which would do so admirably for donkey-races. He will also be called upon to march " by the right " for the first time in his life.

.   .   .   .   .

Branching off from the road, an unexpected cutting provides ingress to the arid waste where the hardest work of the new soldier's life is to be gone through. A strident voice from nowhere, shouting " Pick up the step," synchronizes with the arrival of the little band of dusty pilgrims. It is not the easiest thing in the world to march in step on sand and with arms at the slope. It is not improbable that it is the hardest thing to march at all on it.

Equipment is taken off and dressed, arms are piled and dressed, and a hawk-eyed instructor sees to it that the dressing is not more than, say, an inch out. Very soon the huge parade-ground becomes criss-crossed with countless symmetrical blobs— the square packs and lines of rifles, for while your own unit has been piling arms under superintendence which has demanded movements corresponding to those of a clockwork figure, other batches of men and officers have arrived and received pilotage to where it was decreed before the world began they should go.

If you are lucky enough to be early arrivals you may cast your bodies upon the sand. The stentorian commands to " Look to those slopes " and " Press on your butt " will now give you only amusement, though if you are infantry of the line you will view with envy the parties belonging to rifle regiments, whose interpretation of attention on the march is marching with rifles at the trail and not at the slope. Joy unbounded will be afforded the Tommy by the sight of a squad of officers being made to repeat the movements of ordering arms. Here the Sam Browne gives place to equipment, the slender cane to the nine-pound Service rifle.

" Now, gentlemen, that won't do at all ; cut the hand away smartly ! This is the time," and the instructing officer counts.

" *The Bull Ring* "

At a more reasonable opportunity the squad will be reminded that the eyes of the men are on them the whole time, and there must be no slackness, and that so far as *knowing* is concerned they must know everything the men have to do, but be able to do it, if anything, more efficiently.

.   .   .   .   .

At a given time, all the detachments expected having arrived, the units are marched off. Drill, bayonet-fighting, bomb-throwing, with both live and dummy grenades, practice with gas-helmets, a tour of trenches, and many things disclosure of which wild horses could not drag from me, form the programme of work. Now for the first time probably in his training the man will be *forced* to acquire a little imagination in his exercises with the bayonet. He is told to clench his teeth, "to look fierce," and is made to grunt as he makes his "point" and "jabs," and, too, he will be told exactly why he must make a thoroughgoing windmill of his body if he would throw bombs with success and lack of fatigue.

A very long time after he will be fallen out, half the morning's work having been completed. At the end of the interval he will certainly disbelieve that he has had a break of fifteen minutes. But this, of course, makes no difference to the recommencement of his labours.

The morning comes to an end, as mornings have a habit of doing, and the heterogeneous fragments of the British Army find themselves unpiling arms with the clockwork precision with which they piled them ; which means that the process will be repeated until the standard exacted is attained.

Unlike the entry to the Bull Ring, this time the cutting which leads to it is lined with matadors. As a matter of fact they are really the toreadors who stand at about six paces interval, the self-same instructors. Nor are they there to wish the living stream of khaki "Goodbye"! Far from it. "March by the right." "Look to the slope of that rifle."

But as the road is approached the strains of a band

playing "The British Grenadiers," or some equally rousing march, will make itself heard, and after a few steps the squads will get some sort of idea that there are some fine points about being a soldier.

However, immediately afterwards the bulls, temporarily at all events, cease to be bulls; they are marched "at ease." This time the order is heard by everybody, and with the fervent hope that the nearest guard, for whom they will be called to attention, is miles away, the parties march homewards.

"IDENTITY DISC."
(From *The Daily Mail*.)

HOOCH !

A.F.W.G
1916.

A SERGEANT'S VOICE

Now a Sergeant's voice is a thing that's renowned,
It shatters the air and makes holes in the ground ;
He opens his mouth, gives vent to a roar,
Down crash the houses from ceiling to floor.

To hear that brave voice engaged at its best
Is to find for its efforts a really good test ;
Artillery, massed bands, with thunder thrown in,
Would have a hard task if they wanted to win.

One day our battery broke down on the way,
As the Huns were advancing to engage in the fray ;
But our sergeants were ready, each roared at those Huns ;
They fell down in thousands, as though swept by guns.

The Huns that were captured will ne'er hear again,
Their nerves were all shattered, they wish they'd been
   slain ;
They tremble each time they think of that roar ;
They say it killed thousands, and paralysed more.

Nothing on earth can compare with that voice,
It's a gift, or affliction, according to choice ;
So if to three stripes your ambition should soar,
Remember it's useless unless you can roar.

CPL. MILLIGAN
(6TH DORSETS), WARD D6.
(From 3rd *London General Hospital Gazette*.)

WHAT WE FIND IN THE GERMAN TRENCHES

My C.O. wished to make an examination of the system of Boche village defence, and kindly invited another officer and myself to accompany him.

Naturally, as this is one of our jobs, we like to see how the Boche carries out his and draw interesting comparisons, and, if possible, learn something. We made the usual preparations for such a journey by taking smoke helmets, tin hats, maps, and the like, and clattered along dusty roads among the numerous transport trains and marching troops for several miles behind an old front line until we reached the objective, passing through our own " crump "-smashed villages *en route*, until we arrived at a point where we had to leave the horses in charge of our grooms and proceed on foot.

The way to the Boche defences was strewn with discarded things, big " crump " holes, unexploded shells, and all the evidence of recent conflict. We reached the crest of a hill over-looking a small village and the crest beyond. For miles and miles the outline of trenches could be seen, and our own " crumps " went whuzzling overhead on their fatal journey. In the distance we could see them bursting and clouds of smoke and debris shoot up in the air, and we could see the black smoke of things coming from " across the way." But what a scene of desolation ! No crops had been planted here. Certainly the ground had been tilled, but not with the ploughshare. Rank weeds grew where shells had not recently fallen.

Wire, tangled and torn, tripped the unwary step. Beyond us lay two curious-looking mounds, a few stray battered leafless and branchless trees stood as sentinels in and about these mounds. Once these mounds were villages, so said the plan ; it was difficult to believe it. Truly it was the valley of desolation ; the shadow and the substance of death were there too—freshly dug graves with the little wooden crosses above them placed there by some loving comrade with a name pencilled on.

What we Find in the German Trenches

The Great Crater.

On the right was a curious fresh mound, which showed up white in the brilliant sunshine. We went to examine it, and saw an extraordinary sight. On climbing up it we were on the edge of a crater such as I could not have imagined could have been blown out by man—it seemed more like Nature's handiwork : some mighty subterranean upheaval ; but no, it was a silent witness of what man can devise with the brains he is given. We computed its diameter at 70 yards and depth 50 feet—that is to say, it was about 200 yards in circumference. It was right across the Boche front-trench line. I have not found out when it was fired, but it must have shaken the country for miles around and scared many a Boche into his proper place in the other world, in addition to the ones it blew there. We were discussing later the feelings of the poor Frenchman who will come when this war is over to till that piece of ground.

At first we felt dreadfully sorry for him ; but after some reflection it occurred to us that really it will be a little gold-mine instead of an arid crater. All he has to do is to collect the scraps of Boche wire (barbed) that are lying about, stick a few posts in around the crater, erect a tea-house, and there you are—but not forgetting the ticket-office. He might go farther if he is industrious, and enclose a series of dug-outs still in existence close by, make a huge collection of Boche mementoes, and sell them to the visiting public. Cook would undoubtedly include this crater in his itinerary. That Frenchman is a lucky man.

We dragged ourselves away from this remarkable crater and proceeded to our pilgrimage to the dug-outs via the front-trench line. At least, it used to be a trench. Since our gunners tried their hand on it it has become a series of gaps in the earth, for not a yard of it has escaped them. Still, the well-constructed stairways down to the dug-outs remain intact for the most part.

Underground Hotel.

We went down many. The stairs are very steep, and the timbering of the shaft is very substantial. You reach the bottom, say about 20 feet, and find quite a cosy little entrance hall, with passages leading along to bedrooms and eventually to the next set of steps, so that there is at least one " bolt " hole—in fact several, in some cases. Beds are arranged in boarded tiers like bunks in a ship, or perhaps it reminds one more of an apple-room. The floor is littered with bottles of wine, beer, soda-water, and the like (needless to say they are empty), because I know Fritz would be thirsty when these shells of ours were hurtling around. In addition to the bottles, the floor is littered with dirty bedding, empty boxes, ammunition, hand grenades, and other things too numerous to mention but mostly not worth carrying away, and, moreover, we were by no means the first strangers to view Fritz's late habitation.

We got up into fresh air again and proceeded up trenches into what was once the village. In some places one finds three or four feet of brickwork above ground-level, but generally speaking the place is levelled within 6 feet of the ground. Here the dugouts are larger. One was covered with dirty wall-paper ; electric-light wires showed how comfortable Fritz had been ; you might easily distinguish a dining-room, bedroom, store—and, in fact, all the conveniences of life as if he were aboveground. Indeed, so far as I could see, Fritz had turned the basement of the village (viz. the cellars) into the first floor, and added galleries from dwelling to dwelling to replace the streets above. I have no doubt he enlarged the accommodation of that village underground so that it could house more inhabitants than it had ever done before. It would take days to explore it properly.

We spent about two very interesting hours wandering up and down. In our wanderings aboveground occasionally we came across some of the recent alien inhabitants. I have no pity for Fritz in the least. He is dirty, tricky, clever as a monkey and with as little sense of honour. He has got all and more than he asked for on this front, and if munition workers in England go on as they have been doing, and go still one better, Fritz will not only wish he had not been born, he will in due course cry out for mercy and crave for forgiveness. But, as I have said, not yet.

(From *The Daily Mail*.)

HOW A GERMAN BATTALION PERISHED

(A Letter from the Russian Front)

ONE of our sections had received the order to make its way
to a certain range of hills, go round them, keeping about five
versts to the left, occupy some trenches prepared for them and
hold them against the enemy till noon. We therefore made our
way to the hills, passed them on the left, and found the trenches
as per orders. They were in very good condition, with everything one could wish for, even to the barbed-wire entanglements.
But there was one drawback—the wind had drifted up the snow
to such an extent that the trenches were almost full of it. We
were plunging through it when we heard a timid voice cry—

" War kommt da ? "

" Good God, Germans ! Where the devil do *they* come
from ? " we asked one another in some surprise. " Are there
many of them ? "

" War ist da ? " we heard the voice repeat.

By way of answer we fired a volley, and then a second one.
The Germans were a bit surprised, but recovered and replied in
kind. It was getting dark, and we couldn't see one another.
But we came across one another all right as soon as we had
pushed the snow aside. And then it was a case of bayonets and
butt-ends. We hammered away at each other in silence, and all
the time the bullets kept *phthit*-ting into the drift. No one knew
whether it was our men or the Germans who were firing. And
every man was crying out in his own language, thinking he was
dealing with his own comrades, " Don't fire ! Stop ! " In the
direction where the firing was going on—in front and on the
right—you heard cries in Russian and in German, " What is
happening ? Where are you ? " Our men started yelling to the
Germans, " Surrender ! " And they shouted back, " Throw
down your rifles ! We have surrounded you ! You are our
prisoners ! " " Your arms are not long enough ! You will
bruise your knuckles if you want to take the whole lot of *us* ! "
our fellows replied, and with a new fury we hurled ourselves upon

them, driving them the whole length of their trenches. In their dug-outs the Germans kept shouting out into the darkness, which our eyes couldn't penetrate, "Help! Don't fire! Give them the bayonet!" The result was a roar of hundreds of voices. They sounded like a huge rolling wave. And always fresh voices, drawing nearer and ever nearer. Ah! now they were upon us. "Oh, little brothers, there are swarms of them. We are surrounded on three sides!" cries some one with a sob. "Hadn't we better surrender?" "Knock him on the head!" is the answer from every side. "Put your butt across his jaw! Stick a bayonet in his back and push him into the Germans!"

"Rear rank!"—the word of command rings out like a vibrating cord; the voice is loud and clear—"Rear rank, half-right—Fire!" The crowd in front of us howls, presses forward, and then seems to stop! But behind them other rows of men draw near with yells. Once more the word of command rang out: "Fire!" In front of us fresh cries arose, and groans. However, all along the trenches hand-to-hand fighting was going on. But just here the Germans were making no headway, but kept crying, "Help! Here! this way! Fall on them in the rear!"

But it was we who were giving it them in the back. We had pursued them all along the trenches, and once we had cornered them there soon wasn't a man left.

"Well, we've made a clean sweep of these trenches!" we said. And then we listened. Nothing ahead of us, at any rate; but to the right we could hear the Germans shouting and swearing, and their officers calling out, "Vorwärts! Vorwärts!" These cries were quite close. Still no one fired, and no attack was made. We had already got back to our trenches, and were firing at point-blank range in the direction of the German voices. A few isolated shots replied to ours, and the shouted commands of "Vorwärts!" had ceased. They must be, we thought, at the bottom of their trenches, not daring to advance to the assault.

"Let us give them the bayonet!" we cried. "Let us wipe them out as we did that lot in the corner there!"

"Steady, boys!" rang out that same calm voice of steel. "It may be some new German trap," he added. "We are all right where we are ; we are firing right on to the top of them, and they are not touching us. Aim a little further on and lower. Ready ? Fire ! " The volley produced new cries and groans among the Germans, followed by a few stray shots, which, however, went very high and well above our trenches. After five or six salvos all was quiet, even the groans. There wasn't a sound from the enemy. There might have been no one there. It was as though the earth had swallowed them up.

"What can it mean ? " we cried in astonishment. " Can we have exterminated the whole lot of them ? "

" Excellency, let me go and find out," suggested Stremine, who is our best scout and has already won the Cross of St. George.

"No ; wait. I'll have a look round first myself."

The officer switched on a little electric torch, but before doing anything further took the precaution to raise his arm above the parapet. The men near him, unable to restrain themselves, peered over the parapet too. Not a single shot greeted the appearance of the torch, but we saw, so close that we could almost touch them, row upon row of Germans lying there, one on the top of another !

" Excellency," our men murmured in astonishment, " they are all dead. They do not move. Or else they are shamming ! "

The officer raised himself above the parapet and directed the ray of his torch on to the huddled heaps below him. We saw them buried in the snow either up to their waists or necks, but not one of them moved, and all round them the snow was stained with blood. The officer continued to explore with his lamp, whose rays revealed to us hundreds of Germans lying there dead, and their rifles fallen in the snow by their sides, like a row of sticks.

" I don't understand this," said the officer.

" Excellency, let me go and see ! "

" Go on, then ; and you fellows keep your rifles ready. If anything suspicious happens, fire at once without waiting for the order."

Stremine made his way out of the trench and immediately disappeared, buried up to his neck in the snow. He tried to extricate one leg, but without success. He then wished to rest his weight on one hand, and for that purpose placed it on the snow, but at once withdrew it with an effort, uttering an oath. His hand was terribly scratched, the blood spurting from it.

"It is barbed wire : part of the defences! Help! I cannot do anything by myself!"

We caught hold of him by the collar of his tunic and dragged him out with difficulty. His great-coat, breeches, and boots were torn to ribbons.

"D——n the cursed stuff!" he groaned. "I haven't got any legs left! Every bit of skin is gone!"

"That's what comes of climbing after Germans!" we cried, roaring with laughter.

But the officer understood. The trenches were defended by row after row of barbed-wire entanglements. The snow had entirely hidden these, and even in places lay high above them. The whole of the battalion which had surrounded us had hurled itself forward to the support of their comrades who were calling to them and had got caught in the barbed wire. The first line fell right across it, and those behind, struggling on, came right on the top of those who were already engulfed, succeeded in passing them and at once got caught in their turn. And all this time we were letting them have it with our rifles. The

Seen in the Somme Region.

Germans, in flinging themselves towards the trenches, disappeared in the snow, while the rear ranks, not knowing what was happening, and seeing our fire was almost point-blank in their faces, hurled themselves forward like madmen and got caught too. And in this way a whole German battalion perished.

"Rousskoie Slowo."

6-IN. Q.F.

CORPORAL QUADRING, at the telephone, stared into the feeder, so dark and mysterious as it passed through the floor of the turret into the ammunition-room. There was a noise of machinery in his ears and yet he was alert, quiet, at his ordinary business. His free ear, aloof from the insinuating sound that the carrier made as the shells slowly travelled and rose in the feeder, aloof even from the rumble and crackle of the distant firing which he heard when the cupola rose, was given to his lieutenant who sat there, three feet away, still as a wax figure, listening at the other telephone linked with the heart of the fort, the fire control. He had nothing to do but just to listen and to wait for sounds, for orders, for events in this atmosphere of strange business. The fire was slow, three shots a minute only. And automatically, from time to time, as the little voice below said, "Steady!" he replied, "Steady!"

Nothing was happening yet, but he knew that something must soon happen. Things were not going well with the fortress. He wondered where the French were, whether that field artillery on the right could be theirs; he wondered why in those bursts of sound when the cupola rose he heard so little musketry. No doubt the Germans were within five miles. But then? Why were they not yet being battered? He was lost in the enormous strife. The lieutenant was talking now:

"Control! D'you hear me? Control! . . . Yes, sir! . . . Aeroplane wrecked? . . . What shall I do, sir? . . . Yes, sir."

Then to the sergeant: "Range nine four fifty." And to Quadring: "Speed up."

"Speed up!" cried Quadring into the telephone.

The machinery went a little faster. Slowly before his eyes a shell rose in the black void, harmonious, beautiful in lines, exquisitely polished. As he listened he stared at the sergeant,

225   P

grizzled but alert, watched the shell slide into the hands of four men and travel as if on velvet towards the breech : quick-opened, it swallowed the shell, snapped it up like a greedy mouth. He saw the sergeant push aside a gun-layer, infinitesimally alter the direction.

"Speed up!" said the lieutenant sharply.

They were firing four a minute now, rather blindly towards that place where the German howitzers might be, to show that the fort was fighting rather than to fight. Then the small shell began to fall. . . .

Corporal Quadring listened, interested and calm. He knew the sound : every fifteen seconds, when the cupola rose, he recognized the Krupp 15-pounders. "Small fry," he thought, disdainfully. He did not know where they were falling, hidden in the circular chamber of steel that whirred under his feet, the small, crowded room, intolerably light ; he felt comfortable and secure behind the walls of grey metal. The lieutenant was talking again. Quadring understood : another aeroplane had located the howitzers. The range was altered.

"Speed up! Speed up!" said the lieutenant authoritative rather than impatient.

They were firing at twelve-second intervals now, and there was a gritting sound. It bothered him, this sound, so near him. It dominated the more frequent bark of the 15-pounders out-side. Where were they falling? . . . They sounded nearer now. Then Corporal Quadring heard a large splosh. Oh, they had hit the glacis then! "Fluke," he thought. But there came another shell and then, as the 6-inch fired again, two or three simultaneously, quite close : shrilling through the explosions he heard a cry. He grew taut : "That must have been on the infantry parapet! Poor devils!" thought Corporal Quadring. And then smugly reflected that he was better off inside. Still, the sound worried him. Ah! this was it.

"Oil-can," said the sergeant.

"Oil-can," repeated Quadring, through the telephone.

"Oil-can," said the little voice.

And, as if by magic, the oil-can rose in the feeder. A note of excitement had come into the lieutenant's voice : "Yes, sir,

I understand." Then to the sergeant : " Nine one fifty. Get all you can out of her."

Quadring's heart gave just one beat more and then became normal. They were in for it now.

Suddenly, on his order, the feeder came alive. It rasped and it whirred, running at top speed, for indeed the quick-firer was giving all it could, and the four men seemed to seize the new shell as fast as they fed them. Corporal Quadring was all bewildered outside that calm spot where lay his duty. His first excitement increased, for at last . . . Yes, here it was . . . a dull heavy sound upon the cupola ; the Germans had the range, unless it was another fluke . . . No, not a fluke ; as the cupola closed down two shells fell together on the steel roof. The lieutenant smiled :

" That's the first," he said, " but we . . ."

Corporal Quadring did not hear the rest, for this was not a fifteen-pound shell that had fallen so close over his head that he sank it into his shoulders. The whole turret had quivered under the heavy impact. And now it was indeed : " Speed up !" Hands were feverish as they grasped the shells . . . for the turret had begun to move . . . the cupola rose . . . the 6-inch fired into the gleam of blue sky. The cupola blotted out the blue sky and, rumbling upon its rails while with a swish water escaped from the pipes, the turret moved along the trench to take up a new position. It could take no risks now . .

In front, behind, Quadring heard the explosions. Yes, they were being battered now. The gun was pushed to its utmost, it seemed ; the sergeant in one movement tore off his coat, wiped his face upon his shirt-sleeve. And yet it was not fast enough.

" Speed up ! Speed up !" shouted Quadring.

The lieutenant murmured : " Too slow ! Go below, give 'em hell !"

It seemed curiously cool and dark below. The store-keeper was sulky, hardly listened. Quadring just noticed the wounded hydraulicist who had been hit in the trench and brought in, rather to clear the rails than to save him. He lay, a small khaki bundle, folded up as if to get him out of the way, under a mask of red, his coat black-dyed with blood, half-stunned by a scalp wound.

Then from above came a sound heavier than he had heard before, a vast boom, and for a second everything tottered as if the wall and the feeder itself swayed. The turret shook like a man who had been struck. "Got us full!" he thought, while he stumbled up the stairs tripping on the iron treads, shying back from the electric globes like a nervous horse. Above, all was urgency, and yet calm. Still the feeder was belching shells, still the cupola, a little askew from the blow of the 11-inch shell, rose and fell as the quick-firer replied. He was seized by movement . . . minute after minute passed, lengthened into an hour of heat and fire . . . He was conscious only of the swaying of the turret as it rushed along its trench, fired, rushed back and fired again. It was all action, it was all haste, mechanical as if the men with the gun and the steel walls formed an automatic trinity. Sound was all about him like a black blanket shot with red streaks. Every rise of the cupola let in the growing roar of the German guns, like a wedge, then closed it out. He felt rather than heard the sound grow. He understood. Nothing would help them, now their range was found, save perhaps some lucky shots unlimbering those howitzers hidden behind hill 44 or 45, or, he thought bitterly, 48, who could tell?

He exclaimed. As the cupola rose a shell burst on the edge of the work, and for a second all was invisible, for the turret was filled by a cloud of concrete. Corporal Quadring retched a mouthful of dust . . . fierce, he forced his stung throat, murmured:

"Speed up!"

Thicker and thicker came the sounds. Boom upon boom ringing on the cupola. "It'll buckle," he thought. Then again: "It'll buckle." And as he thought the voice below spoke:

"Bearings jammed!"

"Go on," said the lieutenant.

The gun still raged into the strip of sky; the cupola was doomed and would soon protect it no more. Right, left, fire . . . then left, fire and right again . . . the turret, half-exposed, was fighting still. But a heavy shell fell upon the edge, and suddenly the three inches of steel bent, crumpled like a fan. Right, left . . . then a pause. It synchronized with the bursting of a shell in the trench itself. Quadring knew, he could imagine the rails and roadway twisted up : the turret would never move again . . . it would only wait. Wait ? For what ?

Magic ! The German howitzer answered his question. What had happened ? He felt half-blind and quite deaf ; he was conscious of pipes bursting around him as the hydraulic machinery gave way, of thin streams of water gushing straight at him like spears. And in the dust, fallen into a little lake of water and blood, he saw his officer, with the sergeant and all the men but two. . . . Corporal Quadring did not care. The walls round him buckled as if the turret were folding down over him. The floor writhed under his feet : unclenching his teeth, he murmured blindly into that telephone with the broken wires "Speed up ! " . . .

A very long time later, it seemed, he came out of a pillar of flame, stripped half-naked by the curling steel as a shell, swooping down into the depths, fired the magazine. He did not know how he had come out, how it was he found himself miraculously safe, freed from those other dead, stumbling in the dark along the passage that led to the next turret. He thought : "Poor old Q.F. ! "

Then he was before the captain in Turret No. 3. He saluted.

"No. 2 silenced ? " said the captain. "Oh, all right, I shan't want you yet."

He saluted. This cupola too was rising up and falling, but there was nothing for him to do. He listened to the crash of the shells and after a while grew careless. He wondered how long it would last. He watched those others hard at work in a play where there was no part for him. A shell burst upon the cupola ; it was not his business, this one. Corporal Quadring took from his hip-pocket a letter which he carefully read. A little while later, as the cupola shuddered under one of those familiar booms, he said, half-aloud—

"The Dad can say what he likes, I'm backing Sophomore for the Derby ! "

(By kind permission of the Editor of *Land and Water*.)

OUT WITH A NIGHT PATROL

5 P.M.—Waked from sound sleep.

6.15 p.m.—Met Company Commander. Told him I didn't believe any Germans opposite. Company Commander said in that case I was just the man he wanted, and would I go across at 9.30 p.m. and find out.

6.30 p.m.—Said I would think about it.

6.32 p.m.—Went to think about it in secluded spot.

6.50 p.m.—Still thinking in secluded spot.

7 p.m.—Went to tell off patrol.

7.15 p.m.—Patrol went to think it over in secluded spot (same one).

7.25 p.m.—Observed with telescope four Germans in trenches opposite. Seemed to be large, cheerful men.

7.35-8 p.m.—Pretended to eat hearty dinner. Asked Company Commander whether patrol was necessary, in view of four Germans seen by me. Company Commander said four Germans probably caretaker, wife, and two children locking up for the night. Dislike Company Commander.

8.40 p.m.—Noticed one of patrol writing on black-edged notepaper. Said it was his last will and testament, and would I censor it, as he wished to send it off to-night.

8.45-9 p.m.—Discussed weapons with patrol. Company Commander lent me his Colt automatic pistol and examined mechanism.

9.5 p.m.—Let off Colt accidentally. Severely frightened Company Commander. Felt happier.

9.45 p.m.—Found patrol whistling "Dead March" in unison. Tell patrol we will wait a bit.

9.50 p.m.—Tell patrol I thought we would start.

9.55 p.m.—Tell patrol we ought to start.

10 p.m. Tell patrol we must start.

10.5 p.m.—Company Commander came and asked why we hadn't started.

Out with a Night Patrol

10.10 p.m.—Patrol started. Night very dark.

11.30 p.m.—Fall into large shell-hole getting over parapet. Lose Company Commander's Colt, probably at bottom of shell-hole. Felt happier. Company bomber suggests I should carry the bombs, as am now unarmed. Reprove company bomber for talking. Tread on our listening patrol, all five of us. Listening patrol annoyed. Reprove listening patrol for swearing. Reach our wire front line. Curious smell. Crawl under wire into decaying cow. Remove portions of dead cow from my face. Patrol complains of smell of dead cow. Corporal suggests more open formation. Patrol, in succession from the right, fall into disused trench full of water. Fell in myself. Ask corporal whether he knows way back. Answer in the negative. Collect opinions of patrol as to direction of our lines. Patrol quite positive on four points of the compass (one each). Take my own line. Fall over trip wire into several tin cans. Suspect corporal of using bad language about me. Order corporal to lead the way. Corporal falls over another wire into golconda of tin cans. Swear at corporal. Decide to lie low and listen. Do so. Distinctly hear Private Jones imploring to be allowed to shoot. Shout. Platoon sergeant answers. Saved. Rally patrol, and fall over parapet on to fixed bayonet.

11.45 p.m.—My servant brings me rum in my dug-out. Notice he is wearing respirator. Discover a good deal of dead cow still adhering.

12.30 to 2.15 a.m.—Write report to Headquarters. " Distance covered by patrol estimated at five hundred yards. German trenches overcrowded. Object of patrol attained, etc."

2.15 a.m.—Went to observe path of patrol by daylight. Distance appears less than it seemed at night.

3 a.m.—Fetch Company Commander and ask him how far it is. Company Commander says about fifty yards. Dislike Company Commander. Company Commander asks for his Colt. Feel happier.

3.30 a.m.—Retire to sleep.

4 a.m.—Waked by Company Commander, who asks me if I realize that I am on duty till 8 a.m. The Company Commander be —— " strafered."

SUZETTE DISCUSSES THE SAPPERS

[AUTHOR'S NOTE.—Suzette's companion, being purely imaginary, this wearied Infantryman's plaint must not be considered as anything but fiction. No criticism whatsoever of the Royal Engineers is intended.—RICHARD MULVANY.]

SUZETTE pouted. "I think you're perfectly horrid," she said. "He's quite one of the nicest men I know."

"He may be," I answered, "but when you've said he's an Engineer, you've said all there is to say. For myself, I'd rather be horrid than be an Engineer."

"What's the matter with them?" she asked.

"They're duds—that's all."

"Yes, that's all—rot!" she rejoined scornfully. "There's not another branch of the Service that can show finer records than the R.E.'s."

"Right enough; but those records were made by the old Regulars. And while the other branches of the New Armies have lived up to the old records, the new Engineers have proved an absolute farce."

"I don't believe it," she said, frowning.

If there's one time that I love Suzette more than at another, it is when she frowns, when her eyes close just the slightest bit and her chin comes forward a shade as though it were asking to be—well, asking for what I get so few opportunities of giving it.

"Oh, well, never mind," I said, "let's talk of something interesting. Er—Suzette—do you feel like being kissed?"

"No," she replied very definitely, "I don't. And we are going to talk about Engineers. You've cast aspersions on the nicest man I know——"

"Present company excepted," I said eagerly.

232

" Present company comes miles down the list. As I was saying, you've cast aspersions on the nicest man I know, and you've got to show me some kind of proof, or else apologize."

" Suzette, if I apologize, will you feel like being kissed then ? "

" Oh, don't be so silly ! Why are you moving your chair so close ? "

" My voice isn't very strong this morning. It's rather a strain talking from so far away." (" So far away " was about six feet.)

" Please be sensible " (very frigidly), " and tell me why you don't like the Sappers ? "

" Well," I answered, " if you insist, here goes. Once upon a time, before I had this commission, I was in the ranks, just an ordinary Temporary Tommy. While we were training in England we didn't see very much of the Engineers, and I thought then the same as you think, that Engineers were sort of gods among soldiers."

" And aren't they ? "

" No, they're not. They're a set of idle, lazy, work-shy, good-for-nothing, Woodbine-consuming loafers. They're too confoundedly indolent to do their own work, and their whole duty, as they conceive it, is to stand and look on while an infantryman digs the trench that they are not competent to construct. And the tragedy of it all is that the Staff encourage them to do it."

" But every one says that this war will be won by the Engineers and the Artillery."

" Well, it won't be won by our Engineers anyway. And I think they ought to have told us that when we enlisted. They told us then that the Infantry was the backbone of the Army, and that without us all else would be as nought. Sometimes I think a Tommy's Paradise must be a place where there are no Gunners and no Sappers. Out there at the Front, the Infantry of each side are dumped into parallel ditches, and the Artillery regard them as a target, while the Engineers look upon them as digging machines. My dear, you have no conception of an Engineer's mind. When you or I see a platoon, we see forty or fifty men. But when a Sapper sees a platoon, does he see men ? No, he just sees a kind of personification of so many yards of trench, four feet wide at the top, three feet wide at the bottom, four feet six deep, with a parapet in front nine inches high and five feet thick. And he works by slimy methods. For instance, suppose he has the Staffshire's working for him one day, he'll give them enough work to last them until five in the evening, and then, by soft words and promises of letting them go when they have finished, he manages to get the work finished by three o'clock. Next day he may have the Middlefords. Then he gives each man about a yard more than the Staffshires had and tells them that the Staffshires had only a shade less to do than they have and the Staffshires went home at midday. Of course it isn't true, but he does that each day, and if the Staffshires and the Middlefords hadn't got a little game that they play when the Sapper isn't looking, why, at the end of a week each man would have half a mile of trench to dig, which, according to the R.E., ought to be finished in an hour and a half—easily."

" But what is the game the Staffshires play ? "

" Well, when the Sapper is allotting the work, he makes the first man stick his spade in the ground as a starting-point. Then he walks about four yards and sticks the next man's spade in to mark his task. When he has all the spades in a long line, he says " Carry on," and goes off to see about some other job. The first thing that happens when his back is turned is that the whole line closes in—shuts up like a telescope, to about half its original length. So each man gets a reasonable job to do."

" But doesn't the Engineer notice it ? "

" Not very often ; and if he does, what can he do ? Each man swears he is doing his full share, and each man has an almost invisible dent in the ground to which he can point with a reproving " Look, sir, that's where you put my spade."

" But what happens if the Infantry don't know that game ? "

" I've only known that to happen once. A new division came out and the Engineers tried their usual tricks, and, strange to say, the new men did the work allotted to them. The first day they finished at five o'clock, the second day at nine, the third day at midnight, and then things went from bad to worse. At the end of a fortnight the men had been digging for three days and nights without stopping, and were then five days behind, according to the Sappers. But this division rather fancied itself at digging, and wouldn't give up. They brought up the cook-house and planted it near the spot to keep the men supplied with grub, but although they kept on digging without stopping, at the end of each day they were about a day and a half more behind. It was really tragic."

"But how did it end? Did the men collapse?"

"No, but one dark night the Infantry rose up in their might and smote the Engineers, sappers, corporals, sergeants, and subs, smote them heftily with their own picks, buried them in their own trenches, and planted the stub-ends of their own Woodbines to mark the spot. Then they marched to the General and asked to be put in the front line. Warfare, they said, they understood; fatigues they understood, but the ways of Engineers were beyond their ken."

Suzette smiled. "I wonder," she said, "how much of what you have told me is true."

"What does it matter?" I answered. "My arm is hurting a bit. You might see if you can put my sling right, please."

"You poor boy," she murmured. And then, as she leant towards me from her chair, as her arms went round my neck to rearrange the knot of my sling, as her eyes glanced up at me and then looked down, as her face stopped so very, very close to mine—I was awfully glad I had one arm free!

A GLIMPSE OF WAR

WATER

THE battalion had started long before dawn. At first it had been night, blue, mysterious night, pale and fugitive and hung with little golden stars, the night of the East, made for white courts and the spinning of Scheherazade's tales, a night like blue silk flecked with gems. And then it had passed away hurriedly, as if afraid of the day, of the thunderous sun, like a nymph surprised, leaving behind her as a trail the rose and the mauve of dawn, sweet heralds of a fiercer air.

Private Norley raised his head towards the dawn. He had grown tired of the night, for it had been long, and after a while had thought of nothing save the sand which had mysteriously penetrated between his sock and his foot. But he loved the familiar dawn, for it was not as the brooding night ; it was passing. For a moment Private Norley thought of dawn as he had often seen it before, when he had gone of nights to feed some calving cow. It had come up sometimes just like that on Winchelsea marshes, making their grey into opal, and little Rye, upon its tiny hill, into a rosebud. He thought of the marshes for a little while, of the fresh, cold wind full of Channel salt. It hurt his mouth to think of the feel of that wet wind, for his tongue was so dry. The heat was coming ; he knew that, for already the dawn was dying, sun-slaughtered, and on the eastern horizon a ball of fire, zoned in flame, soared into the Egyptian sky.

He felt very hot suddenly. And he was afraid. He looked at his wrist-watch ; he tried to remember the time-table which the sergeant-major had discussed with the sergeant the night before. They were late evidently ; already they should be in sight of El Arish. And for a moment Private Norley wondered what it all was for, why they were going east of the canal, why they had gone so far and seen nothing, neither Englishman nor Turk, what there was beyond the oasis. The bewilderment of the private who can range through empires, ignorant as a horse in blinkers, was upon him. But Private Norley did not long wonder ; he was a good-tempered, healthy young animal, who had never before thought of life in general : earing, drinking, sleeping, making love and dying as late as possible, that was the sum-total of him. And he was ready enough to do it all decently. So at once he abandoned speculation, searched the horizon for the palm-trees which promised water and shade.

Then he remembered : a full two hours had been wasted at a dry oued. The ammunition carts had, one after the other, stuck in the river-bed, and it had been endless, helping the little oxen, half unloading the carts, shoring up the wheels, so that the beasts might struggle up the crumbling bank of pebble and sand. As the battalion turned towards the south Private Norley caught a glimpse of the carts, massed between the second and third platoon, ammunition wagons, provision carts, ambulances, officers' wagons, canteen, the vast impedimenta of armies. Reflective and impartial, he damned everything on wheels.

The strap of his rifle hurt him a little now as it cut into his moist shoulder. He changed it to the right, and for a long time thought of nothing. There was hardly anything to arouse a thought, for the desert unrolled to the right and to the left, to the front and to the back, without beginning, without end, not quite flat, just like a dirty blanket, with crumples here and there. Sticking out, it seemed, of the horizon a few rocks that looked black against the felty sand ; near the track sometimes a few gleaming white bones, camels', no doubt. Notable only, upon the right and left of the battalion, were the flanking parties, watchful little patrols of the camel corps, so far away that even through a field-glass they looked like little brown toys. Private Norley was too used to them to notice that they were there. Besides, there was something else to help the silence that had now come upon the marching troops ; they had left their bivouac at Abu Dara singing the inevitable "Tipperary," but little by little the song had died down long before the order came that there must be no talking now. For the heat had come and was growing round them.

He realized it, and suddenly there was nothing but heat. The pith helmet made a ring about his forehead ; this was wet, and yet hard and hot, as if his head were bound in metal. He felt the sun upon his cheek, a steady burn, and a sting as of a pin-prick upon his upper lip. He brushed it angrily as if to remove an insect. There was no insect, but the movement, so different from the steady tramping, brought him out into a heavy sweat. Private Norley called himself a fool, but it was too late. Water seemed to rush from his head into his hair and under his helmet to steam. He found his fingers so clammy that the wooden butt of his rifle slipped away ; he dared not touch the burning steel. For a long time he thought of nothing, but just went on with the water running down from that metal ring about his forehead, hot water that soaked his moustache, soaked his eyelashes until he had to blink them free. And even then there was a veil as of steam before his eyeballs. One thought only came to him then : water. As he went he slipped his hand under his coat, touching as he did so his neighbour, who shrank away a little without speaking, knowing that any contact would increase his heat. Carefully Private Norley drew forward the bottle, raised it to his mouth. He could have spat the liquid out, so great was his disgust, for, osier-covered and then felt-covered, and then sheltered by his coat, it was hot. And yet as he swallowed, hating the tinnish taste, the disgusting suggestion of weak soup, he was gluttonous.

Suddenly he thought of water, real cold water as it flows out between the two stones from the spring by Udimore Hill. He remembered that place where in April there always grew so many primroses, and a spasm of rage shook him as he thought that this very minute oxen and horses were drinking their fill of that water, so clear, so cold.

His pal upon the left had seen him drink.

" Pretty fair muck, ain't it ? " he remarked.

Private Norley spat without replying. He heard behind him another man making a feeble joke about lining up at the bar when they got to El Arish. Somebody said something Private Norley did not catch, but it awakened an immediate echo, and a precise private, a schoolmaster in civil life, said they ought to have some water from the water-cart. In a minute the whole battalion was talking of water, and Private

Norley could think of nothing but the water-carts between the two platoons, that looked so queer, swaddled up in canvas, like fat old men, to keep off the sun.

In front of Private Norley marched his lieutenant. He was a slender young man, and he went with an air alert and disdainful, as if he did not hear the growing murmurs among the men. Private Norley did not remember that this was one of the popular officers, a good fellow who never punished a man without making him feel in the wrong : he thought of that way of his and hated him therefor ; his persuasiveness, added to his rare severity, became an insult. For it was hot, so hot, that Private Norley thought only of feeling hot. He found himself cursing quietly, and then grumbling half-aloud, with five hundred others who grumbled also :

"We must have water. We must have water off the cart. . . ."

The battalion was halted, faced to the right. The Major came to quell the mutiny, trotting along the line on his little black horse, whose sweating flanks shone bluish. He stopped, and upon the yellow sand the shadow was blacker than the horse.

"I hear murmurs in the ranks. They must stop. The next man who complains will be shot." The voice was quiet, not very loud, and yet, and so light was the air, every syllable came clean and audible. Then the tone softened : "But, boys, I don't want it to come to that. You've got to understand. We're two hours late, we may be attacked any minute. We may not get to El Arish at all, and if we don't we'll need our water. So I must ask you to be patient." The Major added, with an amiable smile, "I'm feeling pretty dry myself, you know !"

The last words were human and the battalion laughed. They went on. But it was still hotter now, nearly half-past ten and the sun above invisible, for all the sky was as the blue flame of a gas-fire and as burning. Upon the sky-line Private Norley could see four or five palm-trees. The oasis ? Yes, but he had seen those palms an hour before and they looked no nearer. His tongue was thick and large in his mouth ; he parted his lips to breathe and his tongue tried to come out, while he panted like a dog. The sweat upon his eyelashes had caught the dust, his eyes were full of grit, and he wondered vaguely, when he moved his eyelids, why they did not crackle. He did not look up towards the palms. He merely thought, "We shall never get there," and went on. He thought, "My big toe's blistering." Then again, "We shall never get there!"

A little later he saw a mirage, a village upside down on the top of its own picture right side up. He did not care. He did not know that he cared very much whether they got to El Arish or not. He only knew they never would. His belt burnt his hip. He moved it a little and burnt his finger upon the buckle. . . .

The battalion was lined up in front of the oasis. Private Norley and his neighbour quietly shoved each other : they were fighting in deadly earnest for the scrap of shadow afforded by the stem of a palm-tree. But discipline endured : no man moved out of the ranks while water was drawn from the well, and squad after squad stepped forward to fill its water-bottles. The officers, fearing mutiny, dared not delay, and risked colic. At last Private Norley drank. . . .

His mouth was full of something that felt solid, something new, something he gulped at savagely, tried to bite. . . . He choked and still fiercely he bit on at the cold thing which filled his mouth. He could hardly breathe, for he could not tear his lips away from the bottle-neck. He had known what it was to eat when hungry, he had known praise, and love, but now his sweating, burning body was racked to the very entrails by the passionate wedding of his flesh in a cold embrace with this water that penetrated him. He felt his lungs swell and an exquisite freshness rise from his breath. It was agony, for his teeth froze ; and his head ached above the eyes as if he were in the grasp of some frightful sensual desire that imperiously bade him go on to his delight through the pain. . . .

He stopped, threw down the water-bottle and, clasping both hands upon his belt where he felt all swollen and cold, he breathed greedily of the hot air. The bottle was empty.

(By kind permission of the Editor of *Land and Water*.)

Printed in Great Britain by
UNWIN BROTHERS, LIMITED, THE GRESHAM PRESS, WOKING AND LONDON